HYMNS FOR
PRAYER & PRAISE

HYMNS FOR PRAYER & PRAISE

*A hymnal for use in
the celebration of daily prayer
in churches and communities
throughout the year*

Compiled by
Alan Rees OSB   Anthony Greening †
Cecilia Cavanaugh OC   Charles Watson OSB
Mark Hartley OCR   Peter Allan CR

Edited by John Harper

PUBLISHED FOR
THE PANEL OF MONASTIC MUSICIANS BY
THE CANTERBURY PRESS NORWICH

The Canterbury Press Norwich, St Mary's Works,
St Mary's Plain, Norwich, Norfolk NR3 3BH

The Canterbury Press Norwich is a publishing imprint of
Hymns Ancient & Modern Limited

HYMNS FOR PRAYER & PRAISE

ISBN 1 85311 126 0

First published 1996

Music engraved and text set by John Upton, Fordingbridge, Hampshire
Printed and bound in Great Britain by
Richard Clay Ltd, Bungay, Suffolk

CONTENTS

THE HYMNAL

INDEXES

This book is dedicated to the memory of
Hildelith Cumming OSB and Laurence Bévenot OSB.
Both were deeply committed to the work of
The Panel of Monastic Musicians
and to the promotion of music in the liturgy.
Requiescant in pace.

INTRODUCTION

This book contains a comprehensive anthology of the best available hymns in English suitable for use in the daily prayer of the Church throughout the liturgical year. It is intended for use in monastic and religious communities of differing traditions, spiritualities and denominations, and for use in any church or community which observes a pattern of daily corporate prayer with music. It represents the largest collection of Office hymns in English published in Great Britain, exceeding the scope of *The English Hymnal* (1906), *Songs of Syon* (1923) and *A Plainsong Hymnbook* (1932). It differs from recent American books (e.g. *The Hymnal for the Hours*, 1989) in the ethos of the texts, and is unique in providing two tunes for almost every hymn.

Hymns for Prayer and Praise takes as its starting point the new Latin hymn book, *Liber Hymnarius*, edited by the monks of Solesmes (1983). It mirrors this book in a number of ways. First, it provides a comprehensive collection of hymns for the whole of the Church's liturgical year. Second, it includes ancient and medieval hymns of the Church, though here in English. Third, it makes frequent use of the traditional metres which dominate the Latin repertory; and consequently, it includes some of the great plainsong hymn melodies. In other respects, its theological, spiritual, metrical and musical ethos and content are broader than the Latin hymn book.

This book is the work of members of the Panel of Monastic Musicians, a group of monastic and religious men and women from Roman Catholic and Anglican communities in Great Britain assisted by a small group of professional advisers. Since the major liturgical changes of the 1960s and early 1970s the Panel has sought to support and help musicians in communities to find, compose, adapt, and learn new repertory for the re-formed, vernacular liturgy. One of the early fruits was a hymn book for the daily Office, *A Song in Season* (London, Collins, 1976). After twenty years of exploring the new, the Panel has become aware of the need to consolidate the best of what has been achieved; to circulate more widely what has proved durable in individual communities; and to re-establish liturgical and musical continuity from before the reforms, not in a spirit of nostalgia, but of renewal — rekindling old fires in the context of a living English liturgy.

In May 1989 an invitation was sent out to monastic and religious communities to submit unpublished hymn texts and music which might be suitable for a collection for use in corporate daily prayer. The compilers received some 2000 hymns from Great Britain, Ireland, America, Africa and Australasia, and have scrutinized at least another 3000 in established and recently published hymn books from throughout the English-speaking world. In the process of selection it has been necessary to establish criteria, to keep refining them. Initially it was our intention to give precedence to translations of Latin and Greek hymns to emphasize the roots and continuity of the Church's hymnody. But often we were faced with ten or more translations of one hymn and none of others, or else it was clear that an original hymn outstripped the quality of any available translation.

As we selected and edited hymn texts, the compilers became increasingly sensitive not only to new outlooks in theology, spirituality, and language, but also to the nuances and expectations of different denominations, religious orders and individual communities throughout the English-speaking world. The final compilation draws on the work of members of Benedictine, Carmelite, Cistercian, Dominican, Franciscan and Jesuit orders, of other Roman Catholic and Anglican communities, of secular priests and laity, of men and women; it includes texts and music from three continents. Particularly strongly represented are the texts of the Benedictine nuns of Stanbrook Abbey, the Cistercian monks of Mount Saint Bernard Abbey, Ralph Wright OSB of Saint Louis Abbey, Missouri, and James Quinn SJ from Edinburgh. The texts of the majority of hymns included have been written or translated since 1970, but the compilers have included the work of earlier writers and translators, including Edward Caswall, John Mason Neale, Percy Dearmer, Robert Bridges and Laurence Housman.

Although the needs of specific religious orders were a consideration in drawing up the scheme of contents to meet the particular features of their liturgical calendars, the selection of hymn texts within that scheme has been made on the grounds of quality, suitability and durability. The compilers have been careful to include only hymns appropriate to the Office; hymns, therefore, which will endure daily use by the same community (and even grow in richness through repetition) within services dominated by recitation of the psalms, prayer and meditation. Most make use of well-tried metres, but there is a small number of exceptions. Many fine, strong hymns have been excluded as being more fitting for a eucharistic liturgy or for use in parish worship.

Selection of hymn texts by steady critical sifting has been accompanied by editorial scrutiny and emendation. There is a dilemma between respecting the decisions of the author and meeting the needs of the user. However, hymns are distinct from poetry: they are working liturgical texts and even ancient hymns have to justify their place in contemporary worship. Having accepted the principle of the translation of Latin and Greek hymns, then the principle of the revision of English hymns follows naturally: all need to meet criteria of intelligibility, current usage and theology. This has resulted in the emendation of archaic or impenetrable language and outmoded theology, and also sensitivity to gender. That said, there are a very few instances where 'thou' forms have been retained as being unalterable, and there is a small appendix of Latin hymns.

The selection of texts was largely complete before any music was chosen. However, the compilers were clear from the outset over certain issues. In the choice of music we have been conscious that the same fluency in language cannot be assumed in music in communities, and we have tried to accommodate diversity of musical competence without loss of musical integrity. The same criteria of quality, suitability, and durability which applied to text selection have been applied to the tunes, bearing in mind that this is music for the daily Office. In most hymns, two tunes are provided, one unmeasured and monophonic, the other metrical and harmonized. Chant melodies are used where possible, but presented in a manner accessible to all. Harmonized tunes are of a nature suitable for use in the Office. A small number of hymns lacks a second tune because the metre of the text is so unusual.

There has been a long debate about the appropriateness of the English language for singing chant intended for Latin texts. Such adaptation has taken place in Britain since the sixteenth century, has been apparent in English hymn books for over ninety years, and has been the practice of the Community of Saint Mary the Virgin, Wantage, and of the Community of the Resurrection, Mirfield, since their foundation in the nineteenth century. The readings of the chant normally follow the Roman forms of melody, and generally concord with *Liber Hymnarius*, except where the melody comes from a variant repertory (e.g. Salisbury). The edition is pragmatic and practical, not scholarly, and we have used five not four lines, and stemless notes rather than neums. Melodies have been transposed to a performing pitch normally with a lower limit of C, an upper limit of D a ninth higher, and a melodic midpoint around G or A. The same presentation has been adopted for the other monophonic melodies which come from a range of sources from the medieval to the newly composed. Some of the new melodies are paraphrases of old chants, and in a few instances existing melodies have been adapted to different metres. The modern melodies are predominantly the work of members of the Benedictine abbeys of Ampleforth, Belmont, Prinknash, Stanbrook, West Malling, and of the Cistercians of Mount Saint Bernard Abbey.

The metrical, harmonized tunes were mostly composed or compiled between the period 1530 and 1730; they are drawn predominantly from north European collections. This repertory is particularly appropriate to the Office: many have a modal character, and none includes extreme chromaticism or modulation. They are presented in a straightforward, four-part reading, and some have been reharmonized or emended. More elaborate versions are available in many of the standard English hymn books for those who require them. Again care has been taken over the pitch, range and difficulty of all the parts.

Careful consideration has been given to the presentation of the hymns, bearing in mind conventions and expectations throughout the English-speaking world. The presentation of a hymn on a single opening of the book has been a priority, and the original intention to underlay the text of the first verse under both melodies has had to be compromised because of the pressure of space: text is underlaid only under the first tune.

What appears in this book is for the most part tried and tested. Within the bounds of the criteria set for a book of hymns for daily use in the Divine Office, it represents the best of what is available in the English language. The contents are unlikely to transform minds or ears on first acquaintance. They are intended to grow in strength and meaning through regular use. The power of these hymns comes through a marrying of text and music, in which neither is outstanding (in a literal sense) or dominant, but in which both combine to have a quality which exceeds the sum of the independent parts.

The book has taken six years of work, mostly undertaken in short periods of intensive meetings. The compilers thank the communities who have provided hospitality for those meetings, especially Mount Saint Bernard Abbey; those communities and others who have supported the venture financially or by giving freely of their services and time; Thomas Czepiel who typed successive drafts of all the texts (and many rejected texts); Malgosia Czepiel and Sally Harper who assisted in identifying attributions and copyright; Peter McFadyen for assistance with early indexes; and Gordon Knights of The Canterbury Press Norwich, for his interest and support in publishing the book. It is with great sadness that I have to record the death of one of the compilers, Tony Greening, just before the book reached the printer. In addition to his work for the Panel of Monastic Musicians over more than twenty years, he had done much towards this project.

John Harper
Feast of Saint Chad, 1996

USING THE BOOK

STRUCTURE

The book is organized in four liturgical sections, with a smaller fifth section. A full list of the contents is presented in liturgical order before the beginning of the main section of the hymnal. Each section begins a new numerical series: 101 for the Temporal, 201 for the Diurnal, 301 for the Common, 401 for the Proper of the Saints, and 501 for the Latin hymns.

The Temporal consists of a cycle of hymns for the seasons of the Church year. All the seasons include hymns for Evening and Morning Prayer and the Office of Readings, and where appropriate there is provision for seasonal hymns for use at Midday Prayer.

The Diurnal includes hymns for daily use throughout the year. There is a fortnightly cursus for Morning and Evening Prayer, and for the Office of Readings, and a weekly cycle for Compline. Additionally, there are four versions of *Phos hilaron* for Evening Prayer. Hymns for Vigils supplement those for the Office of Readings, and are intended for those communities who sing before daybreak. Similarly, the hymns for Midday Prayer include provision for those who sing all three of the Little Offices.

The Common begins with hymns for feasts of the dedication of a church and of the Blessed Virgin Mary, and ends with hymns for the dead. The central section provides general hymns for the saints - apostles, martyrs, doctors, holy men, holy women, and monastic saints.

The Proper of the Saints provides hymns for specific feast days, and follows the annual calendar from January to December.

The book concludes with fifteen well-known Latin hymns for selected seasons, times, and feasts.

FIRST TUNES

First tunes are printed on five-line staves with stemless noteheads, with a small number of exceptions. Signs for interpretation are restricted to the minimum. Short breath marks between lines are indicated by a small dash through the top line of the stave; longer breaths at caesuras are indicated by a dash in the middle of the stave. Lengthening of a note is indicated by a dot (● ·) or by presenting a double notehead (●●). A quilisma is marked above the note (⩘); those who wish to observe this sign should lengthen the preceding note and lighten the note below the sign.

The melodies are grouped by season or use. Alternatives are suggested, especially in the case of more complex melodies. Users can trace other possible melodies by consulting the metrical index for first tunes.

The melodies are best sung flowingly and freely, following the stress and sense of the words. They are most effective sung unaccompanied. Many can be sung in a more measured way, but this will slow them down and be less responsive to textual nuances. Nevertheless, measured singing of some melodies can be effective, particularly in joyous seasons, and in a few cases they are presented in rhythmic notation.

Those who wish for additional support to their singing can use an instrument or instruments in one of four possible ways: to double the melody in unison or octaves; to provide a drone or drones sustained throughout the hymn; to combine doubling of the melody and a drone; to provide a harmonized accompaniment. Drones can be derived from the final and/or dominant of the mode of the melody. Modes and finals are identified throughout. Harmonized accompaniments may be improvised or composed, but a supplementary book of accompaniments compiled by the Panel of Monastic Musicians is available from The Canterbury Press Norwich.

None of the hymns includes 'Amen' after the doxology, in line with current thinking. Those who nevertheless wish to append 'Amen' may follow this formula in the appropriate mode:

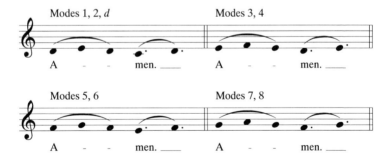

SECOND TUNES

Second tunes are all presented in four-part harmony and may be sung polyphonically. These include a number of tunes which are available only for unison singing in other hymnals. All, however, are suitable for singing in unison, with or without accompaniment. Many originated as unharmonized melodies.

As with first tunes, the second tunes are grouped by season or use. Alternatives are suggested where appropriate. Users can trace other possible melodies by consulting the metrical index for second tunes.

Although the normal unit of notation is a crotchet, most of the hymns will benefit by having an underlying minim pulse, generally set between 50 and 66 beats to the minute. This will encourage the same flexibility, flow and response to the words as the first tunes. Those singing in unison and unaccompanied can adopt a less metrical style closer to that of the first tunes. Shorter breaths are marked by commas above the top stave, and longer breaths by double bars.

None of the harmonizations should be too hard for amateur singers or players. However, in all cases the bass is sufficiently strong and complete to enable keyboard players of limited ability to settle for playing the melody and bass (i.e. top and bottom parts) alone.

'Amen' is not provided but may be sung using either a plagal or perfect cadence in the tonic. Care needs to be taken with a few hymns which end on the dominant (e.g. *Gonfalon Royal*).

ATTRIBUTIONS

Attributions of texts, music and copyright are printed on the opening where the hymn appears. Attributions of Latin originals correspond with *Liber Hymnarius*, which in turn makes use of the book *Te decet laus* by Anselm Lentini, although in some cases dates of authors have been made more specific by reference to *The Oxford Dictionary of the Christian Church*.

All the tunes have been allocated names, with the agreement of composers or communities. Stanbrook melodies for the most part make use of surnames of former Abbesses or names of medieval Benedictine houses in Britain, and the latter is true of West Malling melodies and some of those from Ampleforth and Belmont. Mount Saint Bernard melodies are named after medieval Cistercian houses in Britain. Plainsong melodies have been identified by a text with which they are associated; however, since some are used with several texts (and not necessarily the same group of texts in every Use) these are in some cases arbitrary. Those for the Little Hours and Compline are identified as such.

Where tunes or texts have been emended by the compilers they are marked as 'altered'. Such emendation varies from minor adjustments to more substantial rewriting, according to need.

ACKNOWLEDGEMENTS AND COPYRIGHT

The Panel of Monastic Musicians and The Canterbury Press Norwich thank the owners and controllers of copyright for permission to use the copyright material included in this hymnal. Acknowledgements of copyright are given at the end of each hymn. Every effort has been made to trace copyright owners, and the compilers apologize to any whose rights inadvertently have not been acknowledged.

All amendments made to music and texts by the compilers for this compilation are the copyright of the Panel of Monastic Musicians.

For permission to print copyright hymns, whether in permanent or temporary form, application must be made to the respective copyright holders.

GRANTS

Liberal grants for *Hymns for Prayer and Praise* are made by the publishers to help communities and churches in the introduction of the book or in the subsequent renewal of existing supplies. An application form for a grant can be obtained from The Canterbury Press Norwich, St Mary's Works, St Mary's Plain, Norwich, Norfolk NR3 3BH.

LIST OF SEASONS, DAYS AND FEASTS

THE TEMPORAL

THE DIURNAL

THE COMMON

THE PROPER OF THE SAINTS

LATIN HYMNS

THE TEMPORAL

101-189

101

LM

First tune   CONDITOR ALME SIDERUM   *Mode 4: G*

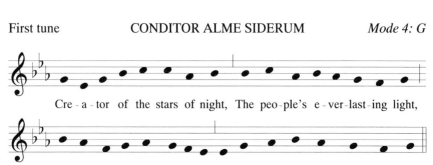

Cre - a - tor of the stars of night, The peo-ple's e - ver-last-ing light,

Re- deem- er, sa-viour of us all, O hear your ser-vants when they call.

Second tune   SAINT AMBROSE

Alternative: PUER NOBIS NASCITUR, 104

1   Creator of the stars of night,
        The people's everlasting light,
        Redeemer, saviour of us all,
        O hear your servants when they call.

2   As once through Mary's flesh you came
        To save us from our sin and shame,
        So now, redeemer, by your grace,
        Come heal again our fallen race.

3   And when on that last judgement day
        We rise to glory from decay,
        Then come again, O saviour blest,
        And bring us to eternal rest.

4   To God the Father, God the Son,
        And God the Spirit, Three in One,
        Praise, honour, might and glory be
        From age to age eternally.

Text: Irwin Udulutsch OFM Cap., with editors' doxology; from *Conditor alme siderum* (9th century). Second tune: La Feillée, *Méthode du Plain-chant*, 1782.

Text: vv. 1-3 © 1971, Irwin Udulutsch, reprinted from *New Catholic Hymnal*, by permission of Faber Music Ltd, 3 Queen Square, London WC1N 3AU; v. 4 © 1995, Panel of Monastic Musicians, Mount Saint Bernard Abbey, Coalville, Leicester LE67 5UL.

102

SM

First tune

MESSIAH

Mode 1: D

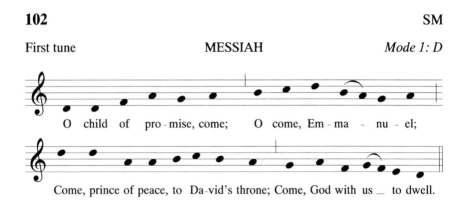

O child of pro-mise, come; O come, Em-ma-nu-el;

Come, prince of peace, to Da-vid's throne; Come, God with us _ to dwell.

Second tune

FRANCONIA

ADVENT

1   O child of promise, come;
O come, Emmanuel;
Come, prince of peace, to David's throne;
Come, God, with us to dwell.

2   The Lord's true servant, come,
In whom is his delight,
On whom his Holy Spirit rests,
The gentiles' promised light.

3   O come, anointed one,
To show blind eyes your face;
Good tidings to the poor announce;
Proclaim God's year of grace.

4   O man of sorrows, come,
Despised and cast aside;
O bear our griefs, and by your wounds
Redeem us from our pride.

5   O come, Messiah King,
To reign in endless light,
When heavenly peace at last goes forth
From Sion's holy height.

Text: James Quinn SJ, abbreviated. First tune: Alan Rees OSB. Second tune: König's *Choralbuch*, 1738, adapted by William H. Havergal (1793-1870).

Text: © 1969, James Quinn SJ and Geoffrey Chapman, a Cassell imprint, Villiers House, Strand, London WC2R 0BB. First tune: © 1995, Belmont Abbey Trustees, Hereford HR2 9RZ.

103

First tune CONDITOR ALME SIDERUM *Mode 4: G*

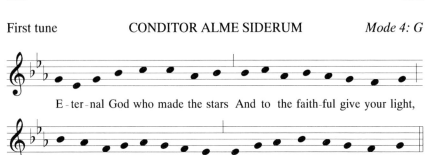

E - ter - nal God who made the stars And to the faith-ful give your light,

Re-deem-er of our fall-en race, Give ear O Christ, to heart-felt prayer.

Second tune SAINT AMBROSE

Alternative: PUER NOBIS NASCITUR, 104

ADVENT

1 Eternal God, who made the stars
   And to the faithful give your light,
   Redeemer of our fallen race,
   Give ear, O Christ, to heartfelt prayer.

2 You came with healing power to save
   A world that languished, self-condemned:
   The wounds of sin were wide and deep,
   The cure for guilt was your free gift.

3 To night-bound peoples of this earth
   In love's redeeming grace you came;
   The bridegroom promised from of old,
   Now born of Mary, virgin pure.

4 Before your strong yet gentle power
   Creation kneels in reverent awe;
   All things in heaven and on earth
   In willing homage bow their heads.

5 We call upon you, holy Lord,
   For you will come to judge the world:
   Protect your pilgrim people here,
   Keep safe our souls from Satan's grasp.

6 All praise and honour, glory, power,
   To God the Father and the Son,
   And to the Spirit, bond of love,
   Through time and in the life to come.

Text: Mount Saint Bernard Abbey, altered; from *Conditor alme siderum* (9th century). Second tune: La Feillée, *Méthode du Plain-chant*, 1782.

Text: © 1995, Mount Saint Bernard Abbey, Coalville, Leicester LE67 5UL.

104 LM

First tune   VENI, REDEMPTOR GENTIUM (ii)   *Mode 2: F*

E-ter-nal, liv-ing Word of God, The light which fills the u - ni-verse,

In sav-ing love and pow'r you came To an-swer your cre- a-tion's cries.

Alternative: VENI REDEMPTOR GENTIUM (1), 105

Second tune   PUER NOBIS NASCITUR

ADVENT

1   Eternal, living Word of God,
The light which fills the universe,
The saviour of the world, you came
To answer your creation's cries.

2   The Son of God, yet humbly born
A servant bearing all our sin,
Fulfilling all the Father's will
In human form, redeemer-king.

3   The tree of Jesse springs anew:
Make straight our way, O Lamb of God,
That we in joy may live on earth,
Reflecting your incarnate love.

4   By your blest Spirit's power and grace,
Illuminate the Church, your bride,
That she in constant hope may wait
Your second coming to proclaim.

5   Then shall the whole created world
The triumph of salvation know;
Made one in Christ, let all give praise
To God, unceasing Trinity.

Text: editors; from *Verbum supernum prodiens a Patre* (10th century). Second tune: melody adapted by Michael Praetorius (1571-1621); harmony, John Harper.

Text and second tune (harmony): © 1995, Panel of Monastic Musicians, Mount Saint Bernard Abbey, Coalville, Leicester LE67 5UL.

105
First tune VENI, REDEMPTOR GENTIUM (i) *Mode 1: F*

LM

O come, Re-deem-er of us all,
Pro-claim to us your vir - gin birth;
Let all the earth in won - der know
The in-car-na - tion of our God.

Second tune PUER NOBIS NASCITUR

ADVENT

1   O come, Redeemer of us all,
    Proclaim to us your virgin-birth;
    Let all the earth in wonder know
    The incarnation of our God.

2   Not by the will of mortals here,
    But by the Spirit's holy breath
    The Word of God is now made flesh:
    The humble maid conceives her son.

3   As from the Father forth he comes,
    So to the Father he returns,
    Descending to the depths of hell,
    Ascending to the throne of God.

4   True God from all eternity,
    Put on our frail humanity;
    And even in its weakness show
    The triumph of your victory.

5   All praise to you, blest Trinity,
    To Father and incarnate Word,
    Both with the Holy Spirit, one
    For time and all eternity.

Alternative first tune: VENI REDEMPTOR GENTIUM (2), 104

Text: The Community of the Holy Name, altered; from *Veni, redemptor gentium*, Saint Ambrose (c. 339-97). Second tune: melody adapted by Michael Praetorius (1571-1621); harmony, John Harper.

106

7.6.7.6

First tune   UNS KOMPT EIN SCHIFF   *Mode 1: D*

Through-out a world in sha - dow, John's ur-gent voice we hear:

Pre - pare for Christ your sa - viour, The Son of God is near.

Second tune   DER EERSTEN ZIJN LAATSTEN

ADVENT

1   Throughout a world in shadow,
John's urgent voice we hear:
Prepare for Christ your saviour,
The Son of God is near.

2   His veiled but certain splendour
Begins to shine from far;
He comes, his saints around him:
The bright and morning star.

3   He gives a new beginning
To those who turn from sin,
Who answer love with loving,
By turning back to him.

4   With all who wait with longing,
Give thanks that never cease,
For him whom God is sending
To visit us in peace.

Text: Stanbrook Abbey. First tune: *Katholische Gesangbuch*, Andernach 1608. Second tune: melody, Fritz Mehrtens (1922-75); harmony, John Harper.

Text: © 1974, Stanbrook Abbey, Callow End, Worcester WR2 4TD. Second tune: melody, © 1993, Boekencentrum BV, Zoetermeer, Netherlands; harmony, © 1995, Panel of Monastic Musicians, Mount Saint Bernard Abbey, Coalville, Leicester LE67 5UL.

107

8.7.8.7

First tune   SIXLAND   *Mode 2: F*

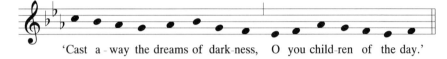

Hark, a he-rald voice is call-ing: 'Christ is nigh,' it seems to say;

'Cast a-way the dreams of dark-ness, O you child-ren of the day.'

Second tune   MERTON

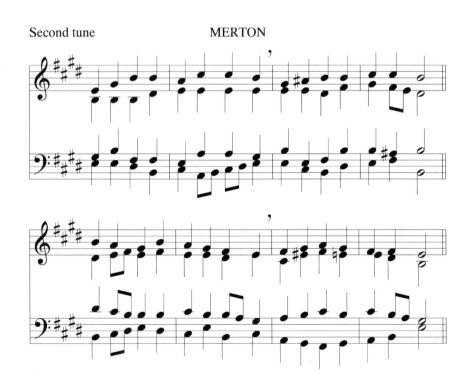

ADVENT

1   Hark, a herald voice is calling:
    'Christ is nigh,' it seems to say;
    'Cast away the dreams of darkness,
    O you children of the day.'

2   Startled at the solemn warning,
    Let the earth-bound soul arise:
    Christ, her sun, all sloth dispelling,
    Shines upon the morning skies.

3   Lo, the Lamb, so long expected,
    Comes with pardon down from heaven;
    Let us haste, with tears of sorrow,
    One and all to be forgiven;

4   So, when next he comes in glory,
    And earth's final hour draws near,
    May he then as our defender
    On the clouds of heaven appear.

5   Honour, glory, virtue, merit,
    To the Father and the Son,
    With the co-eternal Spirit,
    While unending ages run.

Text: Edward Caswall (1814-78), altered; from *Vox clara ecce intonat* (10th century). First tune: John Harper. Second tune: William H. Monk (1823-89).

Text (this version) and first tune: © 1995, Panel of Monastic Musicians, Mount Saint Bernard Abbey, Coalville, Leicester LE67 5UL.

108   LM

First tune   **VOX CLARA ECCE INTONAT**   *Mode d: A*

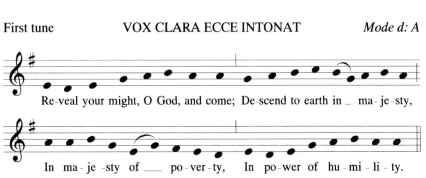

Re-veal your might, O God, and come; De-scend to earth in _ ma-je-sty,

In ma-je-sty of ___ po-ver-ty, In po-wer of hu-mi-li-ty.

Second tune   ROUEN

ADVENT

1   Reveal your might, O God, and come;
    Descend to earth in majesty,
    In majesty of poverty,
    In power of humility.

2   Be seen, O God, omnipotent,
    Enthroned on wood of crib and tree;
    Be foremost now in sacrifice,
    Surrendered, slay iniquity.

3   O Son of Man, obedient,
    The prisoners bound in sin set free;
    The lame, the weak, the blind reprieve;
    Proclaim your day of liberty.

4   Come manifest, most merciful,
    In flesh creation's destiny,
    That we may see your love revealed,
    Your perfect love, blest Trinity.

Text: Anonymous, adapted by Ralph Wright OSB, altered. Second tune: melody, Rouen Antiphoner, 1728; harmony, Stephen Dean.

109

CM

First tune   ANGLICANUS   *Mode 8: G*

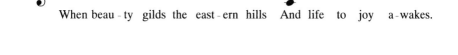

The King shall come when morn-ing dawns And light tri-umph-ant breaks,

When beau - ty gilds the east - ern hills And life to joy a - wakes.

Second tune   MORNING SONG (CONSOLATION)

ADVENT

1   The King shall come when morning dawns
    And light triumphant breaks,
    When beauty gilds the eastern hills
    And life to joy awakes.

2   Not as of old, a little child
    To bear and fight and die;
    But crowned with glory, like the sun
    That lights the morning sky.

3   O brighter than the glorious morn
    Shall this fair morning be,
    When Christ our king in beauty comes
    And we his face shall see.

4   The King shall come when morning dawns
    And light and beauty brings.
    Lord Jesus Christ, your people pray,
    Come quickly, King of kings.

Text: John Brownlie (1857-1925), altered. First tune: *The Anglican Office Book*. Second tune: melody, *Kentucky Harmony*, 1816; harmony, John Harper.

Text (this version) and second tune (harmony): © 1995, Panel of Monastic Musicians, Mount Saint Bernard Abbey, Coalville, Leicester LE67 5UL. First tune © 1981, Communities Consultative Council (Anglican Religious Communities), PO Box 17, Eccleshall, Stafford ST21 6LB.

110 CM

First tune RORATE *Mode 1: D*

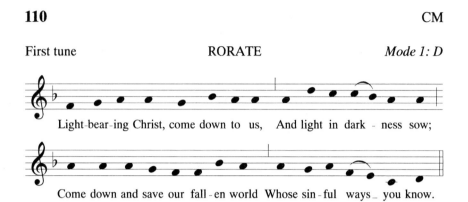

Light-bear-ing Christ, come down to us, And light in dark - ness sow;

Come down and save our fall-en world Whose sin-ful ways _ you know.

Second tune DUNDEE

ADVENT

1   Light-bearing Christ, come down to us,
And light in darkness sow;
Come down and save our fallen world
Whose sinful ways you know.

2   Prepare us for your light and truth,
Who watch and wait for you;
Restore our once lost dignity;
Come down and make us new.

3   Almighty Father, speak the word
Your children long to hear,
And with your Spirit dwell with us:
Lord God of love, draw near.

Text: Stanbrook Abbey. First tune: Alan Rees OSB. Second tune: melody, Scottish Psalter, 1615; harmony, Thomas Ravenscroft, *Psalmes*, 1621.

Text: © 1974 and 1995, Stanbrook Abbey, Callow End, Worcester WR2 4TD. First tune: © 1995, Belmont Abbey Trustees, Hereford HR2 9RZ.

111 LM

First tune NICOLAS *Mode 1: D*

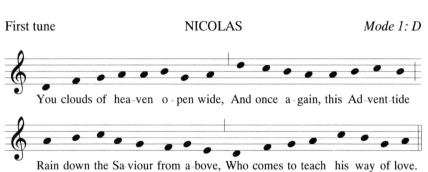

You clouds of hea-ven o-pen wide, And once a-gain, this Ad-vent-tide

Rain down the Sa-viour from a-bove, Who comes to teach his way of love.

Second tune EIN KIND GEBOR'N

ADVENT

1   You clouds of heaven, open wide,
    And once again, this Advent-tide
    Rain down the Saviour from above,
    Who comes to teach his way of love.

2   Lift up your heads, you mighty gates:
    Behold, the king of glory waits.
    The king of kings is drawing near;
    Soon our redeemer shall appear.

3   To Jesus praise for ever be,
    Whose advent sets all people free,
    Whom with the Father we adore,
    And Holy Spirit evermore.

Text: The Dominican Sisters, Stone. First tune: Dutch Traditional. Second tune: melody, German carol; harmony, C.J. Gatty (d. 1928).

112   7.6.7.6

First tune   **ROSA MYSTICA**   *Mode 2: A*

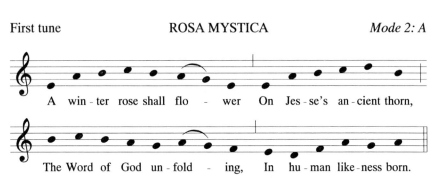

A win - ter rose shall flo - wer   On Jes - se's an - cient thorn,

The Word of God un - fold - ing,   In hu - man like - ness born.

Second tune   **DER EERSTEN ZIJN LAATSTEN**

ADVENT

1   A winter rose shall flower
    On Jesse's ancient thorn,
    The Word of God unfolding,
    In human likeness born.

2   The world will see a marvel
    It cannot understand,
    When God made man approaches,
    Salvation in his hand.

3   O Christ, so long awaited,
    Your age-old promise keep;
    Awake to life your people
    Who lie in sin asleep.

4   Come forth from God, your Father,
    Take Adam's guilt away,
    And with your holy Spirit
    Come, Lord, do not delay.

Text: Stanbrook Abbey. First tune: Alan Rees OSB. Second tune: melody, Fritz Mehrtens (1922-75); harmony, John Harper.

Text: © 1974 and 1995, Stanbrook Abbey, Callow End, Worcester WR2 4TD. First tune: © 1995, Belmont Abbey Trustees, Hereford HR2 9RZ. Second tune: melody, © 1993, Boekencentrum BV, Zoetermeer, Netherlands; harmony, © Panel of Monastic Musicians, Mount Saint Bernard Abbey, Coalville, Leicester LE67 5UL.

113

First tune   CHRISTE, REDEMPTOR OMNIUM (i)   *Mode 1: E*   LM

O Christ, re - deem - er, ___ Lord of ___ all,

And ___ God the Fa - ther's on - - ly ___ Son,

In ___ all - tran - scend - ing ___ mys - te - ry

Be - got - ten ___ from e - ter - ni - ty.

Second tune   VOM HIMMEL HOCH

CHRISTMAS

1 O Christ, redeemer, Lord of all,
   And God the Father's only Son,
   In all-transcending mystery
   Begotten from eternity.

2 In you we see the Father's light,
   The unknown glory of his face;
   Throughout the world we cry to you,
   In mercy hear your people's prayer.

3 Remember now, salvation's Lord,
   That once you took our human flesh,
   And from the Virgin Mother's womb
   Were born in fellowship with us.

4 Each year this festal day proclaims
   To all on earth the solemn word;
   We call to mind the Word who came
   From God's high throne to set us free.

5 Sky, ocean, earth, the universe,
   And every creature ever made,
   In exultation praise our God
   Who sent his Son to save the world.

6 And we, for whom your precious blood
   Has won redemption, life and peace,
   In new and joyful songs unite
   To celebrate this holy birth.

7 All praise to you, blest Trinity,
   To Father and incarnate Word,
   Both with the Holy Spirit, one
   For time and all eternity.

Text: editors' compilation; from *Christe, redemptor omnium ... ex Patre* (6th century). Second tune: melody, Valentine Schumann, *Geistliche Lieder*, 1539; harmony, editors.

Text and second tune (harmony): © 1995, Panel of Monastic Musicians, Mount Saint Bernard Abbey, Coalville, Leicester LE67 5UL.

114   7.6.7.6

First tune   **ROSA MYSTICA**   *Mode 2: A*

A great and migh-ty won - der, Re-demp-tion draw-ing near:

The Vir - gin bears the in - fant, The prince of peace is here.

Second tune   **MARIA EST GEBOREN**

CHRISTMAS

1 A great and mighty wonder,
   Redemption drawing near:
   The Virgin bears the infant,
   The prince of peace is here.

2 The Word becomes incarnate
   And yet remains on high;
   On earth is heard the anthem
   As glory fills the sky.

3 The angels sing the story:
   Rejoice, O distant lands;
   Let valleys, forests, mountains
   And oceans clap their hands.

4 He comes to save all nations:
   Let all now hear his word;
   Approach and bring him worship,
   The saviour and the Lord.

Text: John Mason Neale (1818-66), altered; from the Greek, Saint Germanus (7th century). First tune: Alan Rees OSB. Second tune: melody, Brachel, Köln, 1623; harmony, Charles Wood (1866-1926).

115   7.5.7.5

First tune   CORONA LUCIS   *Mode 2: G*

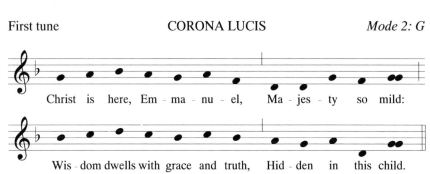

Christ is here, Em - ma - nu - el, Ma - jes - ty so mild:
Wis - dom dwells with grace and truth, Hid - den in this child.

Second tune   BLYDE

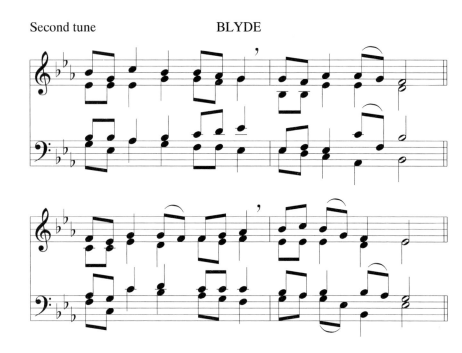

CHRISTMAS

1   Christ is here, Emmanuel,
    Majesty so mild:
    Wisdom dwells with grace and truth,
    Hidden in this child.

2   Here is God's eternal Son,
    Now to earth made known,
    By the Spirit's love conceived,
    Mary's flesh his own.

3   Born of God's creative will,
    Christ is light from light,
    Come to rescue Adam's race
    Waiting in the night.

4   Father, Son and Spirit blest:
    Heaven their glory sings,
    While the earth with mighty voice
    Praise and worship brings.

Text: Stanbrook Abbey. First tune: Alan Rees OSB. Second tune: melody, Stanbrook Abbey; harmony, John Harper.

Text and second tune (melody): © 1974 and 1995, Stanbrook Abbey, Callow End, Worcester WR2 4TD. First tune: © 1995, Belmont Abbey Trustees, Hereford HR2 9RZ. Second tune (harmony): © 1995, Panel of Monastic Musicians, Mount Saint Bernard Abbey, Coalville, Leicester LE67 5UL.

116   10.10

First tune   SAINT SEIRIOL   *Mode 3: E*

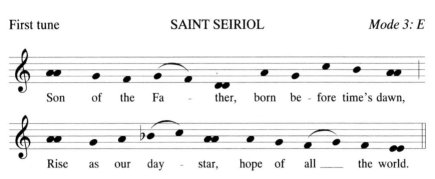

Son   of   the   Fa - ther,   born be - fore time's dawn,

Rise   as   our   day - star,   hope of   all ___ the world.

Second tune   PENMON

CHRISTMAS

1   Son of the Father, born before time's dawn,
      Rise as our daystar, hope of all the world.

2   O star of Jacob, light of heaven above,
      Light up our darkness, shine on all the earth.

3   Kings, kneel in homage; give to Christ, your king,
      Gold, myrrh and incense, faith and hope and love.

4   This day God's glory dawns on Sion's hill;
      Now shall all nations walk in Sion's light.

5   Praise now the Father, praise now Christ the Son,
      Praise now the Spirit, praise one God on high.

Text: James Quinn SJ. First and second tunes: John Harper.

Text: © 1994, James Quinn SJ and Geoffrey Chapman, a Cassell imprint, Wellington House, Strand, London WC2R 0BB. First and second tunes: © 1995, Panel of Monastic Musicians, Mount Saint Bernard Abbey, Coalville, Leicester LE67 5UL.

117

First tune   **A SOLUS ORTUS CARDINE**   *Mode 3: E*

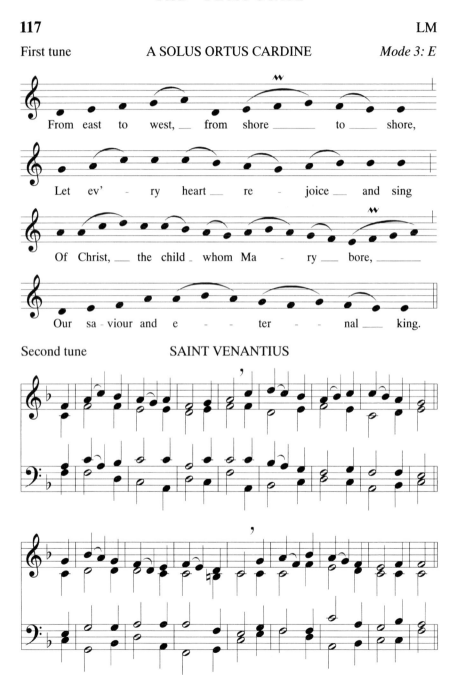

From east to west, — from shore ——— to —— shore,

Let ev' - ry heart — re - joice — and sing

Of Christ, — the child — whom Ma - ry — bore, ———

Our sa - viour and e - - ter - - nal — king.

Second tune   **SAINT VENANTIUS**

CHRISTMAS

1   From east to west, from shore to shore,
      Let every heart rejoice and sing
      Of Christ, the child whom Mary bore,
      Our saviour and eternal king.

2   When Mary heard the angel's word
      She bowed to all the Father willed,
      And suddenly the promised Lord
      That pure and holy temple filled.

3   Now see, the world's creator wears
      The very form to us he gave;
      Our flesh and blood the maker shares,
      His fallen human race to save.

4   He shrank not from the oxen's stall,
      He lay within the manger-bed;
      And he, whose bounty feeds us all,
      At Mary's breast himself is fed.

5   And while the angels in the sky
      Sang praise above the silent field,
      To shepherds poor the Lord most high,
      The one great shepherd, was revealed.

6   All glory for that blessed morn
      To God the Father ever be,
      And to the Son, of virgin born,
      With Holy Spirit, One in Three.

Text: John Ellerton (1826-93), altered; from *A solis ortus cardine*, Caelius Sedulius (5th century). Second tune: melody, Rouen Antiphoner, 1728; harmony, Michael Fleming, altered.

Text (this version): © 1995, Panel of Monastic Musicians, Mount Saint Bernard Abbey, Coalville, Leicester LE67 5UL. Second tune (harmony): © 1986, The Canterbury Press, Norwich NR3 3BH.

118

7.7.7.7

First tune   FREUEN WIR UNS ALL IN EIN   *Mode 1: D*

Sing with joy this bless-ed morn: Un-to us a child __ is born,

Un-to us a Son is giv'n, God him-self comes down from heav'n.

1   Sing with joy this blessed morn:
     Unto us a child is born,
     Unto us a Son is given,
     God himself comes down from heaven.

2   God from God and light from light
     Comes with mercies infinite,
     Joining in a wondrous plan
     Comes to earth as Son of Man.

3   God with us, Emmanuel,
     Deigns for ever now to dwell;
     He to Adam's fallen race
     Freely gives abundant grace.

4   God comes down that we may rise,
     By him lifted to the skies;
     Christ is Son of Man that we
     One with God in him may be.

CHRISTMAS

Second tune ORIENTIS PARTIBUS 7.7.7.7.4

Al - le - lu - ia.

Text: Christopher Wordsworth (1807-85), revised Ralph Wright OSB and editors. First tune: Michael Weisse (1531). Second tune: melody, Office de la Circoncision, Sens, 13th century; harmony, Ralph Vaughan Williams (1872-1958), from *The English Hymnal*, altered.

119   8.7.8.7

First tune   UNTO US A CHILD   *Mode 3: G*

Un - to us   a child is giv - en, Christ our sa - viour brings re - lease;

Coun - sel - lor, e - ter - nal Fa - ther, God made man and prince of peace.

Second tune   STUTTGART

CHRISTMAS

1 Unto us a child is given,
Christ our saviour brings release;
Counsellor, eternal Father,
God made man and prince of peace.

2 Born of Mary, gentle virgin,
By the Spirit of the Lord;
From eternal ages spoken:
This the mighty Father's Word.

3 Love and truth in him shall flower,
From his strength their vigour take.
Branches that are bare shall blossom;
Joy that slept begins to wake.

4 Praise the everlasting Father
And the Word, his only Son;
Praise them with the Holy Spirit,
Perfect Trinity in One.

Text: Stanbrook Abbey. First tune: Laurence Bévenot OSB (1901-90). Second tune: melody adapted from C. F Witt, *Harmonia Sacra*, Gotha 1715.

Text: © 1974, Stanbrook Abbey, Callow End, Worcester WR2 4TD. First tune: © 1995, Ampleforth Abbey Trust, York YO6 4EN.

120   LM

First tune   CHRISTE, QUI SPLENDOR ET DIES (i)   *Mode 8: F*

The Light of ___ light to dark - ness came,

The word ___ e - ter - nal to ___ pro - claim;

The Word which was be - fore all time, ___

In time now dwells, the Christ, ___ di - vine.

Second tune   VOM HIMMEL HOCH

1   The Light of light to darkness came,
      The word eternal to proclaim;
      The Word which was before all time,
      In time now dwells, the Christ, divine.

2   Our God from all eternity,
      Made flesh in our humanity,
      Now cradled in a manger lies,
      His kingship hidden from our eyes.

3   Jesus, the everlasting Word,
      In you the Father's voice is heard;
      In you, the saviour of our race,
      We see the brightness of God's face.

4   True radiance of the Father's light,
      Revealed in weakness to our sight,
      Redeemer, prophet, priest and king,
      Your wondrous birth with joy we sing.

5   All praise to you, incarnate Son,
      With Father and with Spirit one;
      To you, O blessed Trinity,
      Be praise through all eternity.

Text: The Community of Saint Mary the Virgin, Wantage, altered. Second tune: melody, Valentine Schumann, *Geistliche Lieder*, 1539 (attributed to Martin Luther); harmony, editors.

Text: © 1985, The Community of Saint Mary the Virgin, Wantage, Oxfordshire. Second tune (harmony): © 1995, Panel of Monastic Musicians, Mount Saint Bernard Abbey, Coalville, Leicester LU67 5UL.

121

BEATA CAELI

Mode 6: A♭

1 He for whom the in-fi-nite u-ni-verse Can-not find room,

E-ter-nal Lord of cre-a-tion, O Ma-ry, Lies in your womb.

2 He whom the sun and moon have o-beyed Through un-known years,

Now through the power of the Ho-ly Spi-rit A young girl bears.

3 He whose hand holds _ in be-ing The cos-mic span,

Feeds at the breast of his vir-gin-mo-ther As God _ made man.

4 Hap-py the maid who in her womb Has borne God's Son:

Through her the longed-for hour of sal-va-tion At last _ has rung.

5 Praise to him, born of a vir-gin, The al-migh-ty Word.

Sing in the Spi-rit praise to the Fa-ther, Je-sus is Lord.

1 He for whom the infinite universe
 Cannot find room,
 Eternal Lord of creation, O Mary,
 Lies in your womb.

2 He whom the sun and moon have obeyed
 Through unknown years,
 Now through the power of the Holy Spirit
 A young girl bears.

3 He whose hand holds in being
 The cosmic span,
 Feeds at the breast of his virgin-mother
 As God made man.

4 Happy the maid who in her womb
 Has borne God's Son:
 Through her the longed-for hour of salvation
 At last has rung.

5 Praise to him, born of a virgin,
 The almighty Word.
 Sing in the Spirit praise to the Father,
 Jesus is Lord.

Text: Ralph Wright OSB. Tune: melody, Charles Watson OSB.

Text: © 1995, Ralph Wright OSB, Saint Louis Abbey, 500 South Mason Road, Saint Louis, Missouri 63141. Tune: © 1995, Charles Watson OSB, Prinknash Abbey, Cranham, Gloucester GL4 8EX.

122   11.11.11.11

First tune   MARCHE DOUCEMENT   *Mode 2: E*

The great God of hea-ven is come down to earth,

His mo-ther a vir-gin, and sin-less his birth;

The Fa-ther e-ter-nal, his fa-ther a-lone:

He sleeps in the man-ger, he reigns on the throne.

1 The great God of heaven is come down to earth,
   His mother a virgin, and sinless his birth;
   The Father eternal his father alone:
   He sleeps in the manger, he reigns on the throne.

2 A babe on the breast of a maiden he lies,
   Yet sits with the Father on high in the skies;
   Before him their faces the seraphim hide,
   While Joseph, unfearing, keeps watch by his side.

3 Lo, here is Emmanuel, here is the child,
   The Son that was promised to Mary so mild,
   Whose power and dominion shall ever increase:
   The prince that shall rule in a kingdom of peace.

Text: Henry Ramsden Bramley (1833-1917), abbreviated and altered. First tune: adapted from Frederick A. Reesor. Second tune: melody, English traditional; harmony, Martin Shaw (1875-1958), from *The English Hymnal*, altered.

Text (this version): ©1995, Panel of Monastic Musicians, Mount Saint Bernard Abbey, Coalville, Leicester LE67 5UL. First tune: © 1983, Frederick A. Reesor. Second tune (harmony): © Oxford University Press. Altered by permission.

MARY, THE MOTHER OF GOD

Second tune   A VIRGIN UNSPOTTED

45

123   SM

First tune   MARIANDYRYS   *Mode 1: D*

This child from God __ a-bove, The Fa-ther's gift di-vine;

To this new life __ of light and love We give __ his seal and sign.

Alternatives: MESSIAH, 102; SPLENDOR PATRIS, 454

Second tune   SAINT MICHAEL

1   This child from God above,
    The Father's gift divine;
    To this new life of light and love
    We give his seal and sign;

2   To bear the eternal Name,
    To walk the Master's way,
    The Father's covenant to claim,
    The Spirit's will obey;

3   To take the Saviour's cross,
    In faith to hold it fast;
    And for it reckon all things loss
    As long as life shall last;

4   To tell his truth abroad
    To tread the path he trod,
    With all the who love and serve the Lord:
    The family of God.

Text: Timothy Dudley-Smith. First tune: John Harper. Second tune: Genevan Psalter, 1551, adapted by William Crotch (1775-1847).

Text: © 1974, Timothy Dudley-Smith. First tune: © 1995, Panel of Monastic Musicians, Mount Saint Bernard Abbey, Coalville, Leicester LE67 5UL.

124

8.7.8.7.8.7

First tune   TIBI, CHRISTE   *Mode 2: F♯*

To the name of our sal-va-tion Ho-nour, wor-ship _ let us pay,

Which for ma-ny a ge-ne - ra-tion Deep in God's fore-know-ledge lay;

Saints of ev' - ry race and na-tion Sing a-loud that _ name to-day.

1 To the name of our salvation
  Honour, worship let us pay,
  Which for many a generation
  Deep in God's foreknowledge lay;
  Saints of every race and nation
  Sing aloud that name today.

2 Jesus is the name we treasure,
  More than words can ever tell;
  Name of grace beyond all measure,
  Ear and heart delighting well;
  This our refuge and our treasure,
  Conquering sin and death and hell.

3 Highest name for adoration,
  Strongest name for victory,
  Sweetest name for meditation
  In our pain and misery;
  Name for greatest veneration
  By the citizens on high.

4 Name of love, that he who preaches
  Speaks like music to the ear;
  Who in prayer this name beseeches
  Finds its comfort ever near;
  Who its perfect wisdom reaches
  Heavenly joy possesses here.

5 Jesus — name of all our praising
  In this world to which you came,
  Here we sing of love amazing,
  And your saving power proclaim;
  Hearts and voices heavenward raising:
  All our hope is in your name.

THE HOLY NAME OF JESUS

Second tune   ORIEL

Text: John Mason Neale (1818-66), adapted; from *Gloriosi salvatoris* (Meissen Breviary, 1510). First tune: adapted from the Roman chant. Second tune: C. Ett, *Cantica Sacra*, Munich 1840.

125   7.6.7.6

First tune   GARENDON   *Mode 1: D*

The pride of Rome and A - thens   And all   the an - cient world

Falls dumb be - fore the glo - ry   That shines in Beth - le - hem.

Second tune   CHERRY TREE

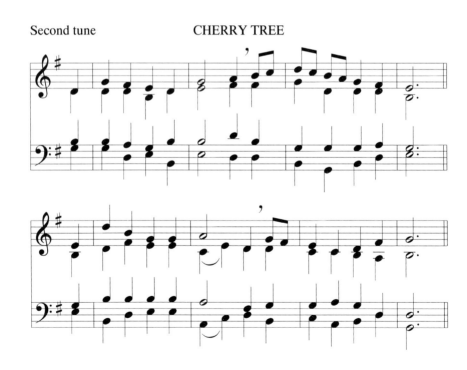

EPIPHANY

1　The pride of Rome and Athens
　　And all the ancient world
　　Falls dumb before the glory
　　That shines on Bethlehem.

2　In you is born the Saviour
　　Who is both God and man:
　　A star of wondrous splendour
　　Is herald of his birth.

3　The Magi see and follow,
　　To bring their kingly gifts,
　　And falling down they offer
　　Their incense, gold and myrrh.

4　The precious gold and incense
　　Proclaim him king and God,
　　While fragrant myrrh foreshadows
　　The spices of the tomb.

5　To Christ be praise and glory,
　　Who stands revealed this day,
　　With Father and the Spirit
　　Throughout eternity.

Text: Mount Saint Bernard Abbey, altered; from *Hostis Herodes impie*, Peter the Venerable (c. 1092-1156). First tune: Mount Saint Bernard Abbey. Second tune: melody, English traditional; harmony, John Harper.

Text and first tune: © 1995, Mount Saint Bernard Abbey, Coalville, Leicester LU67 5UL. Second tune (harmony): © 1995, Panel of Monastic Musicians, Mount Saint Bernard Abbey, Coalville, Leicester LU67 5UL.

126

SM

First tune — LLANFIHANGEL DINSYLWY — *Mode 7: D*

The Word in - car - nate dwelt On earth __ that we might live;

Come, let us wor - ship and a - dore The Christ, the Son of Man.

Alternatives: MESSIAH, 102; SPLENDOR PATRIS, 454

Second tune — POTSDAM

Alternative: FRANCONIA, 102

EPIPHANY

1 The Word incarnate dwelt
  With us that we might live;
  Come, let us worship and adore
  The Christ, the Son of Man.

2 Filled with the Spirit's power,
  The Father's only Son,
  True God from God, and light from light,
  A child, yet life divine.

3 He took this human form,
  And bore an outcast's death,
  A covenant in broken flesh
  Salvation to us brought.

4 Revealed to all on earth
  This child is peace and hope;
  We know him as the risen Christ,
  And ever sing his praise.

Text: editors. First tune: John Harper. Second tune: anonymous; based on the theme of Bach's Fugue in E, Book 2, *Das wohltemperierte Klavier.*

Text and first tune: © 1995, Panel of Monastic Musicians, Mount Saint Bernard Abbey, Coalville, Leicester LE67 5UL.

127

LM

First tune   CHRISTE, QUI SPLENDOR ET DIES (i)   *Mode 8: F*

O Beth-le - hem, you were the least, But now_ you are be-yond com-pare:

For him we ho-nour on this feast,   Our sav-ing God, you shel - tered there.

Second tune   DIE GANZE WELT (HILARITER)

EPIPHANY

1   O Bethlehem, you were the least,
     But now you are beyond compare:
     For him we honour on this feast,
     Our saving God, you sheltered there.

2   The star that told our Saviour's birth
     Was fairer than the morning sun,
     Proclaimed him, lowly here on earth,
     The Lord of all, God's holy one.

3   The eastern kings come from afar:
     Three precious gifts for him they bear,
     And guided by the radiant star
     Bring gold and frankincense and myrrh.

4   Each gift shows forth a mystery:
     They named him king and offered gold,
     Gave incense to God's majesty,
     And with the myrrh his death foretold.

5   All praise to you, our king and Lord,
     Revealed in your divinity,
     And may you ever be adored
     Within the holy Trinity.

Text: Saint Mary's Priory, Fernham; from *O sola magnarum urbium*, Prudentius (348-c. 410). Second tune: melody, *Kölner Gesangbuch*, 1623; harmony, Redmund Shaw, altered.

Text: © 1995, Saint Mary's Priory, Fernham, Faringdon, Oxfordshire SN7 7PP. Second tune (harmony): © 1971, Redmund Shaw; by permission of Paul Inwood.

128

LM

First tune   LITTLE HOURS (CHRISTMAS)   *Mode 2: E*

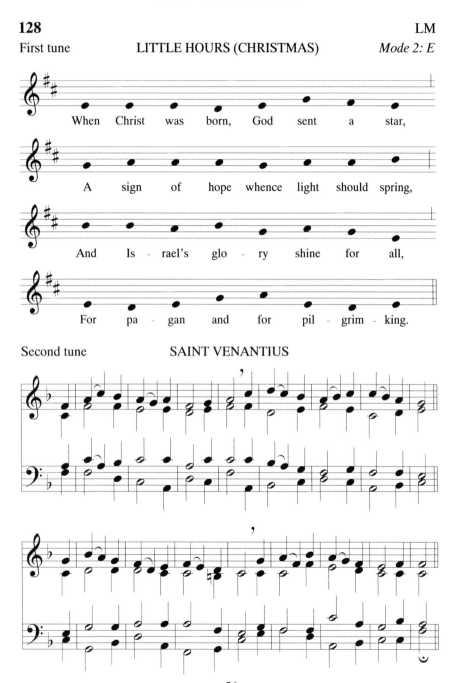

When Christ was born, God sent a star,

A sign of hope whence light should spring,

And Is - rael's glo - ry shine for all,

For pa - gan and for pil - grim - king.

Second tune   SAINT VENANTIUS

EPIPHANY

1   When Christ was born, God sent a star,
     A sign of hope whence light should spring,
     And Israel's glory shine for all,
     For pagan and for pilgrim-king.

2   He is the Father's only Son
     On whom the Spirit came to rest,
     Who was baptised to cleanse our sins:
     The Lamb of God and saviour blest.

3   He is the anchor of our soul
     And shares with us his life divine;
     For sadness he exchanges joy,
     As water he once changed to wine.

4   We praise the Father, Lord of life,
     And Christ, his well-beloved Son,
     Who with the Spirit is our peace:
     Most tranquil Trinity in One.

Text: Stanbrook Abbey. Second tune: melody, Rouen Antiphoner, 1728; harmony, Michael Fleming, altered.

Text: © 1974, Stanbrook Abbey, Callow End Worcester WR2 4TD. Second tune (harmony): © 1986, The Canterbury Press, Norwich NR3 3BH.

129

LM

First tune   A PATRE UNIGENITE   *Mode 4: F♯*

The Vir - gin ___ bore God's on - ly ___ Son.

From heav'n ___ he came ___ to dwell _____ on ___ earth.

In _____ hu - man form he blessed ___ the ___ stream

Where liv - ing faith ___ is brought _____ to ___ earth.

Second tune   VOM HIMMEL HOCH

BAPTISM OF OUR LORD

1 The Virgin bore God's only Son.
 From heaven he came to dwell on earth.
 In human form he blessed the stream
 Where living faith is brought to birth.

2 You saved our race from sin and death.
 Enlarge our hearts with joy so deep
 That filled by hope's blest light we may
 In perfect trust and safety sleep.

3 Lord, stay with us as night-time falls.
 You shared our flesh that we might be
 Made sharers in your Godhead's state,
 Redeemed from sin, from death set free.

4 O Christ, our life, our truth, our way,
 In you we see the Father's face,
 In you the Spirit's love we see,
 Dear fount of life and love and grace.

Text: Thomas Cooper, *The Roman Hymnal*; from *A Patre unigenite* (10th century?). Second tune: melody, Valentine Schumann, *Geistliche Lieder*, 1539 (attributed to Martin Luther); harmony, editors.

Text: © 1992, Thomas Cooper, 59 Station Road, Llandaff North, Cardiff CF4 2FB. Second tune (harmony): © 1995, Panel of Monastic Musicians, Mount Saint Bernard Abbey, Coalville, Leicester L67 5UL.

130

LM

First tune

A PATRE UNIGENITE

Mode 4: F♯

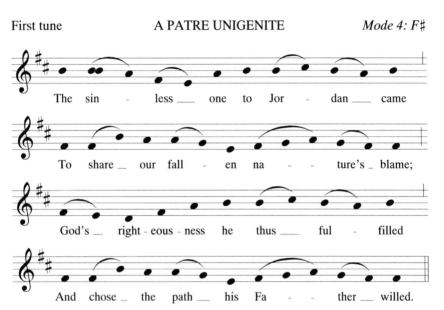

The sin - less __ one to Jor - dan __ came
To share __ our fall - en na - - - ture's _ blame;
God's __ right - eous - ness he thus __ ful - filled
And chose _ the path __ his Fa - - ther __ willed.

1   The sinless one to Jordan came
         To share our fallen nature's blame;
         God's righteousness he thus fulfilled
         And chose the path his Father willed.

2   Uprising from the waters there,
         The voice from heaven did witness bear
         That he, the Son of God, had come
         To lead his scattered people home.

3   Above him, see the heavenly Dove,
         The sign of God the Father's love,
         Now by the Holy Spirit shed
         Upon the Son's anointed head.

4   How blest that mission then begun
         To heal and save a race undone;
         Straight to the wilderness he goes
         To wrestle with his people's foes.

BAPTISM OF OUR LORD

130

Second tune   SAINT MARK

5   On you shall all your people feed
        And know you are the Bread indeed,
        Who gives eternal life to those
        That with you died, and with you rose.

Text: G. B. Timms, abbreviated. Second tune: W. Crowfoot (1724-83), from Crisp's *Divine Harmony*, 1755.

Text: © The Canterbury Press, Norwich NR3 3BH.

131

First tune   A PATRE UNIGENITE   *Mode 4: F♯*

When Jesus comes to be baptised,
He leaves the hidden years behind,
The years of safety and of peace,
To bear the sins of humankind.

Second tune   PATRI MONSTRAT

BAPTISM OF OUR LORD

1   When Jesus comes to be baptised,
     He leaves the hidden years behind,
     The years of safety and of peace,
     To bear the sins of humankind.

2   The Spirit of the Lord comes down,
     Anoints the Christ to suffering,
     To preach the word, to free the bound,
     And to the mourner comfort bring.

3   He will not quench the dying flame,
     And what is bruised he will not break,
     But heal the wound injustice dealt,
     And out of death his triumph make.

4   Our everlasting Father praise
     With Christ, his well-beloved Son,
     Who with the Spirit reigns serene,
     Eternal Trinity in One.

Text: Stanbrook Abbey. Second tune: melody, La Feillée, *Méthode du Plain-chant*, 1752; harmony, John Harper.

Text: © 1974 and 1995, Stanbrook Abbey, Callow End, Worcester WR2 4TD. Second tune (harmony): © 1995, Panel of Monastic Musicians, Mount Saint Bernard Abbey, Coalville, Leicester LU67 5UL.

132

CM

First tune   PRINKNASH PARK   *Mode 2: E*

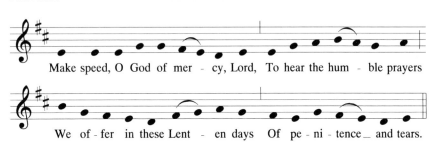

Make speed, O God of mer - cy, Lord, To hear the hum - ble prayers

We of - fer in these Lent - en days Of pe - ni - tence — and tears.

1 Make speed, O God of mercy, Lord,
  To hear the humble prayers
  We offer in these Lenten days
  Of penitence and tears.

2 You know our thoughts, you understand:
  Our weakness proves your power;
  As we return, forgive with love
  The failures of the hour.

3 Give us the strength to win control
  Of every swift desire,
  That fasting from all taste of sin
  Our love may never tire.

4 Receive, most holy Trinity,
  The offerings we raise;
  O Lord of all simplicity,
  Increase our loving praise.

Second tune   BURFORD

Text: T. A. Lacey (1853-1931), adapted by Ralph Wright OSB; from *Audi, benigne conditor*, Saint Gregory? (c. 540-604). First tune: Charles Watson OSB. Second tune: Chetham, *Psalmody,* 1718.

Text (this version): © 1989, GIA Publications Inc., 7404 South Mason Avenue, Chicago, Illinois 60638. All rights reserved. First tune: © 1995, Charles Watson OSB, Prinknash Abbey, Cranham, Gloucester GL4 8EX.

133

LM

First tune IAM, CHRISTE, SOL IUSTITIAE *Mode d: A*

O God, __ cre - a - tor of __ us all, From whom we come,

to whom __ we go, You look __ with pi - ty

on our hearts: __ The weak - ness of __ our wills you know.

Alternative: QUA CHRISTUS HORA, 142

Second Tune O IESU, MI DULCISSIME

LENT

1   O God, creator of us all,
From whom we come, to whom we go,
You look with pity on our hearts:
The weakness of our wills you know.

2   Forgive us all the wrong we do,
And purify each sinful soul.
What we have darkened, heal with light,
And what we have destroyed, make whole.

3   The fast by law and prophets taught,
By you, O Christ, was sanctified:
Bless all our penance, give us strength
To share the cross on which you died.

4   O God of mercy, hear our prayer,
With Christ your Son, and Spirit blest,
Transcendent Trinity in whom
Created things all come to rest.

Text: Stanbrook Abbey; from *Deus, creator omnium*, Saint Ambrose (c.339-97). Second tune: *Clausener Gesangbuch*, 1653.

Text: © 1974, Stanbrook Abbey, Callow End, Worcester WR2 4TD.

134   10.11.11

FOUNTAINS   *Mode 1:D*

Kind - ly   Cre - a - tor,   look   up - on   our   tears;

Bow   down   to   hear   as   we   pray   to   you   in   trust,

Dur - ing   this   our   year - ly   fast   of   for - ty   days.

LENT

1   Kindly Creator, look upon our tears;
       Bow down to hear as we pray to you in trust,
       During this our yearly fast of forty days.

2   Loving and watchful reader of our hearts,
       Weakness and sickness you see and understand:
       Pardon those who turn to you and ask for grace.

3   Heavy indeed the load of sin we bear,
       Stronger your mercy to wash away our guilt:
       Heal our wounds, that new-found health may praise your name.

4   God of our fathers, Three in perfect love,
       Grant what we ask from your mercy quick to save:
       May your children grow in grace through Lenten fasts.

Text: Mount Saint Bernard Abbey; from *Audi, benigne conditor*, Saint Gregory? (c. 540-604). Tune: Mount Saint Bernard Abbey.

Text and tune: © 1995, Mount Saint Bernard Abbey, Coalville, Leicester LE67 5UL.

135 LM

First tune PRINKNASH PARK *Mode 2:E*

We call on you, our liv - ing Lord Who makes the Fa - ther known;

O shep-herd, we have wan - dered far, Find us and lead _ us home.

Second tune BURFORD

LENT

1   We call on you, our living Lord
     Who makes the Father known;
     O shepherd, we have wandered far,
     Find us and lead us home.

2   Your glance at Peter helped him know
     The love he had denied;
     Now gaze on us and heal us, Lord,
     Of selfishness and pride.

3   Reach out and touch with healing power
     The wounds we have received,
     That in forgiveness we may love,
     And may no longer grieve.

4   Lord Jesus, as we turn from sin
     With strength and hope restored,
     Receive the homage that we bring
     To you, our risen Lord.

5   Then stay with us when evening comes
     And darkness makes us blind;
     O stay until the light of dawn
     May fill both heart and mind.

6   Receive, most holy Trinity,
     The offerings we raise;
     O Lord of all simplicity,
     Increase our loving praise.

Text: Ralph Wright OSB, re-ordered and altered. First tune: Charles Watson OSB. Second tune: Chetham, *Psalmody*, 1718.

Text: © 1981, ICEL Inc., Washington DC 20005. First tune: © 1995, Charles Watson OSB, Prinknash Abbey, Cranham, Gloucester GL4 8EX.

136

LM

First tune — IAM, CHRISTE, SOL IUSTITIAE — *Mode d: A*

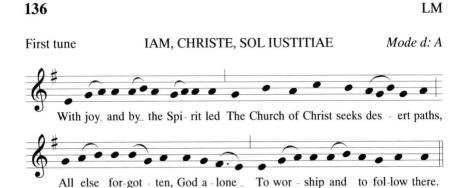

With joy and by the Spi-rit led The Church of Christ seeks des - ert paths,

All else for-got - ten, God a - lone To wor - ship and to fol-low there.

Alternative: QUA CHRISTUS HORA, 142

Second tune — DAS WALT' GOTT VATER

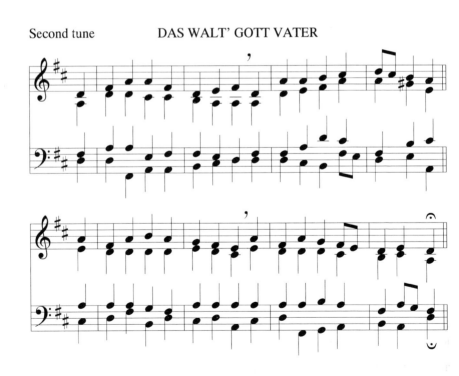

LENT

1   With joy and by the Spirit led,
    The Church of Christ seeks desert paths,
    All else forgotten, God alone
    To worship and to follow there.

2   There silence shall set free the will
    The heart to one desire restore,
    There each restraint shall purify
    And strengthen those who seek the Lord.

3   There bread from heaven shall sustain
    And water from the rock be struck.
    There shall his people hear his word,
    The living God encounter there.

4   All praise to God who calls his Church
    To make her exodus from sin,
    That tested, fasting and prepared,
    She may go up to keep the feast.

Text: Saint Mary's Abbey, West Malling. Second tune: melody adapted from D. Vetter (d. c. 1730); harmony adapted from J. S. Bach (1685-1750).

137 10.10.10.10

First tune VERBUM DEI *Mode 8: G*

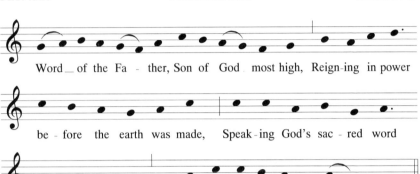

Word_ of the Fa - ther, Son of God most high, Reign-ing in power
be - fore the earth was made, Speak - ing God's sac - red word
through fire and flame, Bring-ing God's ho - li - ness, our souls _ to save:

1   Word of the Father, Son of God most high,
Reigning in power before the earth was made,
Speaking God's sacred word through fire and flame,
Bringing God's holiness, our souls to save:

2   Teach us to seek, beyond this world of time,
The prize of life, the splendour of your face;
Fed by your word, a lamp to guide our feet,
Strong in your steadfast love, O God of grace.

3   Saviour most holy, still, small voice of love,
Lead us by desert paths of purity;
Speak to our hearts, your will for us our peace;
Bring us to live the truth that sets us free.

4   Praise to the Father, fount of love divine;
Praise to his Son, our joy and great reward;
Praise to the Spirit, wisdom from on high;
God the all-holy, one eternal Lord.

Text: Ware Carmel, altered. First tune: editors, from *Verbum supernum prodiens nec Patris*. Second tune: melody and bass, Orlando Gibbons (1583-1625).

Text: © 1995, The Carmelite Monastery, Ware, Hertfordshire SG12 0DT. First tune: © 1995, Panel of Monastic Musicians, Mount Saint Bernard Abbey, Coalville, Leicester LE67 5UL.

LENT

Second tune   SONG 22

138

11.10.11.10

First tune · MISERERE · *Mode 1: D*

Have pi-ty, God of grace, on me, a sin-ner;

My sin-ful heart in your great love con-sole.

Cleanse me, O fount of grace, from sin's de-file-ment;

Bathe me, O heal-ing spring, and make me whole.

1   Have pity, God of grace, on me, a sinner;
     My sinful heart in your great love console.
     Cleanse me, O fount of grace, from sin's defilement;
     Bathe me, O healing spring, and make me whole.

2   True hearts alone, O God of truth, delight you;
     My heart of hearts to truth make ever true.
     Give me a wiser heart to learn true wisdom;
     By steadfast love my waywardness undo.

3   Let me, I pray, live always in your presence;
     Give me your Spirit, Lord, to guide me still.
     Give me anew the joy of your salvation;
     Renew my spirit and uphold my will.

4   All glory be to God, the gracious Father,
     All glory be to God, his only Son,
     All glory be to God, the Holy Spirit,
     Who dwell in us by grace and make us one.

Text: James Quinn SJ; from Psalm 50 (51). First tune: Alan Rees OSB. Second tune: melody, Louis Bourgeois, Genevan Psalter, 1551, rhythm altered; harmony, G. R. Woodward (1848-1934).

Second tune   L'OMNIPOTENT À MON SEIGNEUR

139

First tune   MIRFIELD   *Mode 1: D*

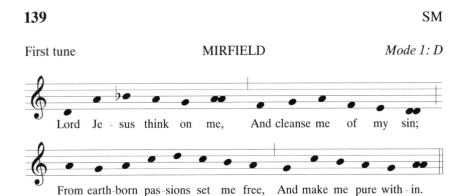

Lord Je - sus think on me, And cleanse me of my sin;

From earth-born pas-sions set me free, And make me pure with-in.

Second tune   SOUTHWELL

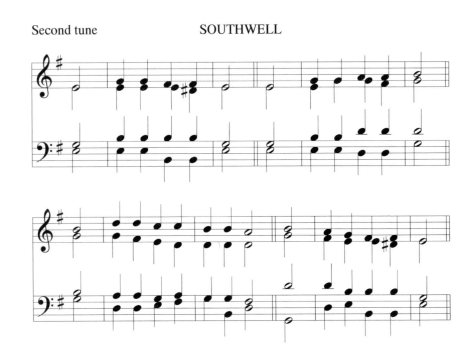

LENT

1   Lord Jesus, think on me,
    And cleanse me of my sin;
    From earthborn passions set me free,
    And make me pure within.

2   Lord Jesus, think on me,
    With care and woe oppressed;
    Let me thy loving servant be,
    And taste thy promised rest.

3   Lord Jesus, think on me,
    Amid the battle's strife;
    In all my pain and misery
    Be thou my health and life.

4   Lord Jesus, think on me,
    Nor let me go astray;
    Through darkness and perplexity
    Point thou the heavenly way.

5   Lord Jesus, think on me,
    When flows the tempest high:
    When on doth rush the enemy,
    O saviour, be thou nigh.

6   Lord Jesus, think on me,
    That, when the flood is past,
    I may the eternal brightness see,
    And share thy joy at last.

Text: A. W. Chatfield (1808-96); from the Greek, Synesius of Cyrene (375-430). First tune: Charles Watson OSB and Peter Allan CR. Second tune: adapted from William Daman, *Psalmes of David in Metre*, 1579.

First tune: © 1995, Panel of Monastic Musicians, Mount Saint Bernard Abbey, Coalville, Leicester LE67 5UL.

140

CM

First tune PEAKED ACRES OLD *Mode 4: F♯*

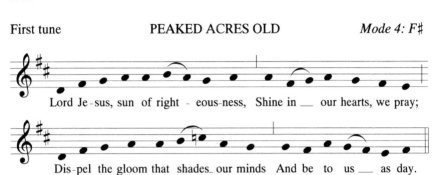

Lord Je - sus, sun of right - eous-ness, Shine in ___ our hearts, we pray;

Dis - pel the gloom that shades ___ our minds And be to us ___ as day.

Second tune ABBEY

LENT

1   Lord Jesus, sun of righteousness,
Shine in our hearts, we pray;
Dispel the gloom that shades our minds
And be to us as day.

2   Give guidance to our wandering ways,
Forgive us, Lord, our sin;
Restore us by your loving care
To peace and joy within.

3   Lord, grant that we in penitence
May offer you our praise,
And through your saving sacrifice
Receive your gift of grace.

4   Now nearer draws the day of days
When paradise shall come,
When we shall be at one with you,
Lord, risen from the tomb.

5   The universe your glory shows,
Blest Father, Spirit, Son;
We shall acclaim your majesty,
Eternal Three in One.

Text: Anne K. LeCroy, altered; from *Iam Christe, sol iustitiae* (6th century). First tune: Charles Watson OSB. Second tune: Scottish Psalter, 1615.

Text: © 1982, Church Hymnal Corporation, 445 Fifth Avenue, New York, NY 10016. First tune: © 1995, Charles Watson OSB, Prinknash Abbey, Cranham, Gloucester GL4 8EX.

141

First tune   CRANHAM CORNER   *Mode 2: F*

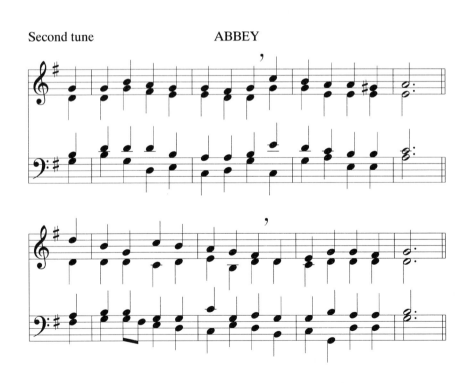

O raise your eyes on high_ and see There stands our sov'-reign Lord:

His glo-ry is this day _ re-vealed, His word a two-edged sword.

Second tune   ABBEY

LENT

1. O raise your eyes on high and see
   There stands our sovereign Lord:
   His glory is this day revealed,
   His word a two-edged sword.

2. We glimpse the splendour and the power
   Of him who conquered death,
   The Christ in whom the universe
   Knows God's creating breath.

3. Of every creed and nation king,
   In him all strife is stilled;
   The promise made to Abraham
   In him has been fulfilled.

4. The prophets stand and with great joy
   Give witness as they gaze;
   The Father with a sign has sealed
   Our trust, our hope, our praise.

5. This glory that today our eyes
   Have glimpsed of God's own Son
   Will help us ever sing with love
   Of Three who are but One.

This hymn is also suitable for The Transfiguration of Christ.

Text: Ralph Wright OSB. First tune: Charles Watson OSB. Second tune: Scottish Psalter, 1615.

Text: © 1976, Panel of Monastic Musicians, Mount Saint Bernard Abbey, Coalville, Leicester LE67 5UL; © 1989, GIA Publications Inc., 7404 South Mason Avenue, Chicago, Illinois 60638. All rights reserved. First tune: © 1995, Charles Watson OSB, Prinknash Abbey, Cranham, Gloucester GL4 8EX.

142

LM

First tune   QUA CHRISTUS HORA   *Mode 2: G*

En-ter our hearts, O ho-ly Lord, To break the bonds that bind us still;

Speak to us your for-giv-ing word That we may do your per-fect will.

Second tune   DAS LEIDEN DES HERRN

LENT

1　Enter our hearts, O holy Lord,
　To break the bonds that bind us still;
　Speak to us your forgiving word
　That we may do your perfect will.

2　Renew in us your Spirit's flame,
　Burn every evil thought away;
　That we may love your holy name,
　And freely run your joyful way.

3　We praise you, Father, for your Son,
　And Spirit, all-consuming fire;
　Eternal Godhead, Three in One,
　Surpassing all that we desire.

Text: The Order of the Holy Paraclete, Whitby; inspired by Eric Milner-White (1884-1963). Second tune: melody adapted from German traditional; harmony, editors.

Text: © 1988, The Order of the Holy Paraclete, Saint Hilda's Priory, Sneaton Castle, Whitby, North Yorkshire YO21 3QN. Second tune (harmony): © 1995, Panel of Monastic Musicians, Mount Saint Bernard Abbey, Coalville, Leicester LE67 5UL.

143

LM

First tune · QUA CHRISTUS HORA · *Mode 2: G*

Lord Je-sus, at this hour you took The cross on which you con-quered death;

You took the way that led to life, The Spi-rit's _ gift your dy-ing breath.

Second tune · LITTLE HILL

LENT

1   Lord Jesus, at this hour you took
The cross on which you conquered death;
You took the way that led to life,
The Spirit's gift your dying breath.

2   Almighty Father, at this hour
You sent the Spirit of your Son
To bring true peace to all on earth,
And make your scattered children one.

3   God's promised Gift, you came to warm
Our lukewarm hearts with living fire;
Bring now to life a lifeless world,
And loveless hearts with love inspire.

4   Praise God the Father, gracious Lord,
Praise God his dear and only Son,
Praise God the Spirit, bond of love,
Praise God, who is for ever one.

Text: James Quinn SJ. Second tune: John Harper.

Text: © 1994, James Quinn and Geoffrey Chapman, a Cassell imprint, Wellington House, Strand, London WC2R 0BB. Second tune: © 1995, Panel of Monastic Musicians, Mount Saint Bernard Abbey, Coalville, Leicester LE67 5UL.

144

CM

First tune   **LASTINGHAM**   *Mode 4: F♯*

May we ob-serve these for - ty days With pe - ni-tence and prayer,

That you may bless with ho - li - ness This sea - son of the year.

Second tune   **SAINT BERNARD**

LENT

1   May we observe these forty days
With penitence and prayer,
That you may bless with holiness
This season of the year.

2   By our offences we abuse
Your endless gifts of love;
Be patient, O redeeming Lord,
Send pardon from above.

3   Undo the damage we have done,
Increase your gift of grace,
That we may always live and serve
In joy before your face.

4   Receive, most holy Trinity,
The offering we raise;
O Lord of all simplicity,
Increase our loving praise.

Text: Ralph Wright OSB. First tune: Laurence Bévenot OSB (1901-90), metre altered. Second tune: adapted from H. Lindenborn, *Tochter Sion*, Köln 1741, in J. Richardson, *Easy Hymn-Tunes for Catholic Schools*, 1851.

145

First tune   **VEXILLA REGIS PRODEUNT**   *Mode 1: E*

Christ's ban - ner guides ___ us on ___ Christ's way,

The roy - al way ___ of him ___ who ___ died; ___

O won - drous cross, ___ from which ___ be - gan ___

Our life ___ when life ___ was cru - ci - fied, ___

Second tune   **AUCTORITATE SAECULI**

PASSIONTIDE

1   Christ's banner guides us on Christ's way,
The royal way of him who died;
O wondrous cross, from which began
Our life when life was crucified.

2   Within Christ's heart, till heart should break,
The fount of life and love lay sealed;
By soldier's lance the living streams
Of blood and water were revealed.

3   Then was fulfilled that word of old
Which David once of Christ did sing,
That God in every land would reign,
Christ crucified is Lord and king.

4   O cross, with noblest blood adorned,
The scarlet throne of royal grace,
We do you honour, for you bore
The saviour-king of Adam's race.

5   Upon your arms, in equal scales,
Salvation's price was duly weighed;
The sinless one, for us made sin,
In sacrifice our ransom paid.

6   O cross of Christ, in you we hope,
By you did Christ his victory win;
O holy cross, our love increase,
In us destroy all power of sin.

7   All praise, O blessed Trinity,
Be yours, from whom all graces flow;
On those who triumph through the cross
The victor's crown in heaven bestow.

Text: James Quinn SJ; from *Vexilla regis prodeunt*, Venantius Fortunatus (c. 530-609). Second tune: melody, Poitiers Antiphoner, 1746; harmony, editors.

Text: © 1969, James Quinn SJ and Geoffrey Chapman, a Cassell imprint, Wellington House, Strand, London WC2R 0BB. Second tune (harmony): © 1995, Panel of Monastic Musicians, Mount Saint Bernard Abbey, Coalville, Leicester LE67 5UL.

146 CM

First tune — CRUX CHRISTI — *Mode 7: C*

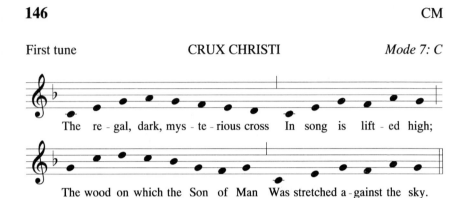

The re - gal, dark, mys - te - rious cross In song is lift - ed high;

The wood on which the Son of Man Was stretched a - gainst the sky.

Second tune — ALBANO

PASSIONTIDE

1   The regal, dark, mysterious cross
In song is lifted high;
The wood on which the Son of Man
Was stretched against the sky.

2   Upon this wood his body bore
The nails, the taunts, the spear,
Till water flowed with blood to wash
The whole world free of fear.

3   At last the song that David sang
Is heard and understood:
'Before the nations God as king
Reigns from his throne of wood.'

4   O blessed tree, upon whose arms
The world's own ransom hung;
His body pays our debt, and life
From Satan's grasp is wrung.

5   May every living creature praise
Our God both one and three,
Who rules in everlasting peace
All whom his cross makes free.

Alternative: The banners of our king proclaim, 437

Text: Ralph Wright OSB, abbreviated; from *Vexilla regis prodeunt*, Venantius Fortunatus (c. 530-609). First tune: Charles Watson OSB. Second tune: Vincent Novello (1751-1861).

147

LM

First tune

TIBI, REDEMPTOR OMNIUM

Mode 8: G

See, Christ was wound-ed for ___ our ___ sake,

And ___ bruised and beat-en for our ___ sin;

So by his suf-f'rings ___ we are ___ healed,

For ___ God has laid our ___ guilt on ___ him.

Second tune

BABYLON'S STREAMS

PASSIONTIDE

1 See, Christ was wounded for our sake,
And bruised and beaten for our sin;
So by his sufferings we are healed,
For God has laid our guilt on him.

2 Look on his face, come close to him;
See, you will find no beauty there:
Despised, rejected, who can tell
The grief and sorrow he must bear?

3 Like sheep that stray we leave God's path,
To choose our own and not his will;
Like sheep to slaughter he has gone,
Obedient to his Father's will.

4 Cast out to die by those he loved,
Reviled by those he dies to save;
See how sin's pride has sought his death,
See how sin's hate has made his grave;

5 For on his shoulders God has laid
The weight of sin that we should bear.
So by his passion we have peace,
Through his obedience and his prayer.

Text: Brian Foley. Second tune: Thomas Campion (1567-1620), altered.

148   8.7.8.7.8.7

First tune   PANGE LINGUA GLORIOSI (i)   *Mode 3: E*

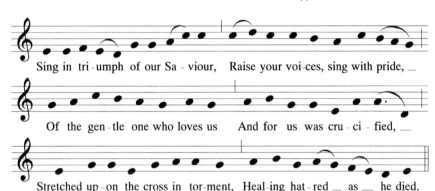

Sing in tri-umph of our Sa - viour, Raise your voi-ces, sing with pride, __

Of the gen-tle one who loves us   And for us was cru - ci - fied, __

Stretched up-on the cross in tor-ment, Heal-ing hat-red __ as __ he died.

Alternative: PANGE LINGUA GLORIOSI (ii), 149

1 Sing in triumph of our Saviour,
  Raise your voices, sing with pride,
  Of the gentle one who loves us
  And for us was crucified,
  Stretched upon the cross in torment,
  Healing hatred as he died.

2 Grieved by Satan's swift deception,
  Our creating, saving Lord,
  Pledged that death would not be final
  As the fruit of human fraud,
  But that life one day would triumph,
  On another tree restored.

3 Harmony with perfect rhythm
  Permeates the balanced plan,
  For the prince of falsehood tumbles:
  Meeting truth he cannot stand;
  And the weapon that once wounded
  Heals within the surgeon's hand.

4 As the chosen hour of judgement
  Struck with lightning's instant flash,
  From beyond all time the Godhead,
  At the Father's timeless wish,
  Came into the womb of Mary
  And put on our mortal flesh.

5 Stirring now he lies restricted
  In the cattle manger's hold.
  Now his mother binds his body
  In the bands against the cold.
  So the hands of her creator
  With her linen she enfolds.

6 May our praises and our wonder
  Echo through the heart of light
  To the Father who creates us
  And the Son whose gentle might
  In the Spirit won us freedom
  From the grasp of endless night.

148

Second tune   FORTUNATUS NEW

Alternative: TANTUM ERGO, 149

Text: Ralph Wright OSB; from *Pange lingua gloriosi proelium* (i), Venantius Fortunatus (c. 530-609). Second tune: melody, Carl F. Schalk; harmony, John Harper.

149 8.7.8.7.8.7

First tune   PANGE LINGUA GLORIOSI (ii)   *Mode 3: E*

Sing in tri-umph of our Sa - viour, Raise your voi-ces, sing with pride, __

Of the gen-tle one who loves us   And for us was cru - ci - fied. __

Stretched up - on the cross in tor-ment, Heal-ing hat - red __ as he died.

Alternative: PANGE LINGUA GLORIOSI (i), 148

1 Sing in triumph of our Saviour,
Raise your voices, sing with pride,
Of the gentle one who loves us
And for us was crucified,
Stretched upon the cross in torment,
Healing hatred as he died.

2 Sing of gall, of nails of spittle,
Sing of sponge and spear and rod,
How the blows of soldiers opened
Wounds within the heart of God,
And the world of pain found healing,
Bathed within the Saviour's blood.

3 See the noble cross resplendent,
Standing tall and without peer.
Where, O Tree, have you a rival
In the leaf or fruit you bear?
Sweet the burden, sweet the ransom,
That through iron your branches bear.

4 Bend your boughs, O Tree, be gentle,
Bring relief to God's own limbs,
Bow in homage to bring comfort
To the gentle King of kings;
Ease the throne where your creator
Harshly treated, calmly reigns;

5 For of all the woods and forests
You were chosen out to hold
That fair prize that would win harbour
For a drifting, storm-tossed world;
You whose wood has now been purpled,
By the Lamb's own blood enfurled.

6 May our praises and our wonder
Echo through the heart of light
To the Father who creates us
And the Son whose gentle might
In the Spirit won us freedom
From the grasp of endless night.

Second tune   TANTUM ERGO

Alternative: FORTUNATUS NEW, 148

Text: Ralph Wright OSB; from *Pange lingua gloriosi proelium* (i), Venantius Fortunatus (c. 530-609).
Second tune: Samuel Webbe, *Motetts or Antiphons*, 1792.

150 11.11.11.5

First tune CRASSWALL *Mode 2: F♯*

There in God's gar - den stands a tree of wis - dom

Whose leaves hold forth the heal - ing of the na - tions:

Tree of all know - ledge, tree of all com - pas - sion, Tree of all beau - ty.

1 There in God's garden stands a tree of wisdom
  Whose leaves hold forth the healing of the nations:
  Tree of all knowledge, tree of all compassion,
  Tree of all beauty.

2 Its name is Jesus, name that says 'Our saviour':
  There on its branches see the scars of suffering;
  See where tendrils of our human selfhood
  Feed on its lifeblood.

3 Thorns not its own are tangled in its foliage:
  Our greed has starved it, our despise has choked it.
  Yet, look, it lives: its grief has not destroyed it,
  Nor fire consumed it.

4 See how its branches reach to us to welcome.
  Hear what the voice says, 'Come to me, ye weary;
  Give me your sickness, give me all your sorrow:
  I will give blessing.'

5 All heaven is singing, 'Thanks to Christ whose passion
  Offers in mercy healing, strength and pardon:
  Peoples and nations take it, take it freely.'
  Amen, my master.

PASSIONTIDE

Second tune   UT QUEANT LAXIS

Text: Erik Routley (1917-82); from the Hungarian of Kiraly Imre von Pecsely (c. 1590-1641). First tune: Alan Rees OSB. Second tune: melody, Paris Antiphoner, 1681; harmony, John Harper.

151

First tune · LASTINGHAM · *Mode 4: F♯*

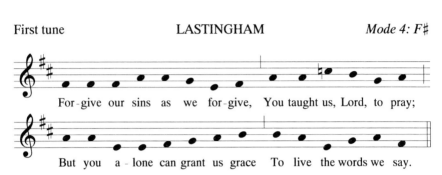

For-give our sins as we for-give, You taught us, Lord, to pray;

But you a - lone can grant us grace To live the words we say.

Second tune · SAINT FLAVIAN

PASSIONTIDE

1　　Forgive our sins as we forgive,
　　　You taught us, Lord, to pray;
　　　But you alone can grant us grace
　　　To live the words we say.

2　　How can your pardon reach and bless
　　　The unforgiving heart
　　　That broods on wrongs, and will not let
　　　Old bitterness depart ?

3　　In blazing light your cross reveals
　　　The truth we dimly knew:
　　　How small the debts are owed to us,
　　　How great our debt to you.

4　　Lord, cleanse the depths within our souls,
　　　And bid all hatred cease;
　　　Then, bound to all in bonds of love,
　　　Our lives will spread your peace.

Text: Rosamond E. Herklots (1905-87), altered. First tune: Laurence Bévenot OSB (1901-90), metre altered. Second tune: adapted from Day's Psalter, 1562, by Richard Redhead (1820-1901).

Text: © Oxford University Press. First tune: © 1995, Ampleforth Abbey Trust, York YO6 4EN.

152

SM

First tune MIRFIELD *Mode 1: D*

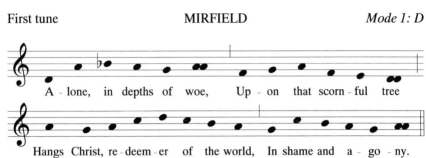

A - lone, in depths of woe, Up - on that scorn - ful tree

Hangs Christ, re - deem - er of the world, In shame and a - go - ny.

Second tune SOUTHWELL

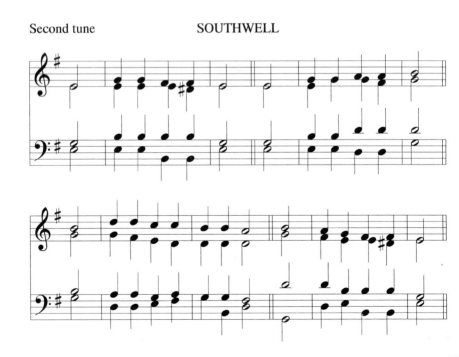

PASSIONTIDE

1   Alone, in depths of woe,
Upon that scornful tree
Hangs Christ, redeemer of the world,
In shame and agony.

2   His feet and hands outstretched
By hammered nails are torn;
In mocking, on his head is thrust
A crown of bitter thorn.

3   Come, kneel before the Lord:
He shed for us his blood;
He died the victim of pure love
To make us one with God.

Text: adapted from Edward Caswall (1814-78); from *Saevo dolorum turbine*, Roman Breviary (Bologna, 1827). First tune: Charles Watson OSB and Peter Allan CR. Second tune: adapted from William Daman, *Psalmes of David in Metre*, 1579.

153   7.6.7.6

First tune   LAURENTIUS   *Mode 2: G*

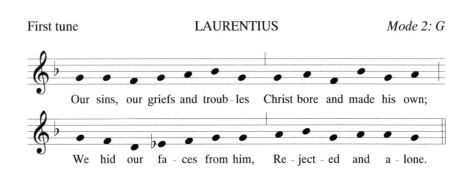

Our sins, our griefs and troub - les   Christ bore and made his own;

We   hid   our   fa - ces from him,   Re - ject - ed   and   a - lone.

Second tune   DU FONDS DE MA PENSÉE

PASSIONTIDE

1   Our sins, our griefs and troubles
Christ bore and made his own;
We hid our faces from him,
Rejected and alone.

2   His wounds are for our healing,
Our peace is by his pain:
Behold, the Man of sorrows,
The Lamb for sinners slain.

3   In Christ the past is over,
A new world now begins;
With him we rise to freedom
Who saves us from our sins.

Text: from Timothy Dudley-Smith 'No weight of gold and silver'. First tune: Laurence Bévenot OSB (1901-90). Second tune: melody, Strasburg, 1539, abbreviated; harmony, Louis Bourgeois (c. 1510-61).

Text: © 1972, Timothy Dudley-Smith. First tune: © 1995, Ampleforth Abbey Trust, York YO6 4EN.

154

CM

First tune — **CRUX CHRISTI** — *Mode 7: C*

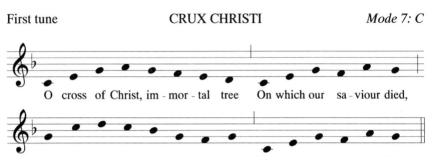

O cross of Christ, im - mor - tal tree On which our sa - viour died,

The world is shel-tered by your arms That bore the cru - ci - fied.

Second tune — **REQUIEM**

HOLY SATURDAY

1   O cross of Christ, immortal tree
      On which our saviour died,
      The world is sheltered by your arms
      That bore the crucified.

2   From bitter death and barren wood
      The tree of life is made;
      Its branches bear unfailing fruit
      And leaves that never fade.

3   O faithful cross, you stand unmoved
      While ages run their course:
      Foundation of the universe,
      Creation's binding force.

4   Give glory to the risen Christ
      And to his cross give praise,
      The sign of God's unfathomed love,
      The hope of all our days.

Text: Stanbrook Abbey. First tune: Charles Watson OSB. Second tune: A. Gregory Murray OSB (1905-92), harmony adapted.

Text: © 1974, Stanbrook Abbey, Callow End, Worcester WR2 4TD. First tune: © 1995, Charles Watson OSB, Prinknash Abbey, Cranham, Gloucester GL4 8EX. Second tune: © 1995, Downside Abbey Trustees, Stratton-on-the-Fosse, Bath BA3 4RH.

155 11.8.11.8

CAMBRAI *Mode 3: D*

His cross stands emp - ty in a world grown si - lent

Through hours of an - guish and of dread;

In still - ness, earth a - waits the re - sur - rec - tion,

While Christ goes down to wake the dead.

HOLY SATURDAY

1   His cross stands empty in a world grown silent
       Through hours of anguish and of dread;
       In stillness, earth awaits the resurrection,
       While Christ goes down to wake the dead.

2   He summons Adam and his generations,
       Brings light where darkness endless seemed;
       He frees and claims his own, so long held captive,
       Who with the living are redeemed.

3   With God the Father and the Holy Spirit,
       Give praise to Christ the crucified,
       Who through the ages seeks to save his lost ones:
       Our sinful race for whom he died.

Text and tune: Stanbrook Abbey.

Text and tune: © 1974 and 1995, Stanbrook Abbey, Callow End, Worcester WR2 4TD.

156 LM

First tune HAYLES *Mode 2: D*

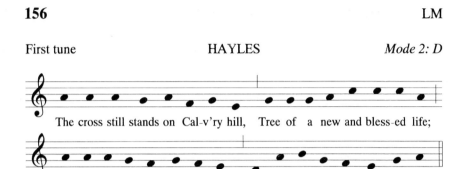

The cross still stands on Cal-v'ry hill, Tree of a new and bless-ed life;
And in a gar-den close at hand The Lord of life and death lies still.

Second tune LITTLE HILL

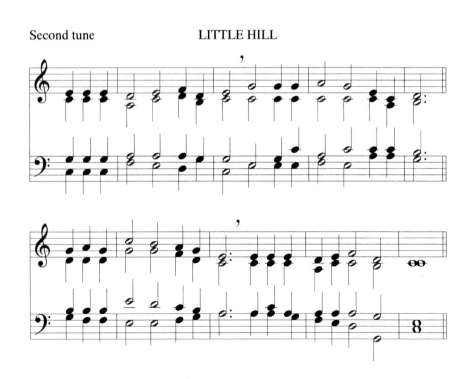

HOLY SATURDAY

156

1   The cross still stands on Calvary hill,
Tree of a new and blessed life;
And in a garden close at hand
The Lord of life and death lies still.

2   The peace of death enfolds him now,
Anguish and pain can do no more;
The victor, victim for our sins,
He sleeps awhile to rise again.

3   To Christ, who died for love of us,
Bearing our sins before the throne,
To Father and to Paraclete
Be glory till the end of time.

Text and first tune: Mount Saint Bernard Abbey. Second tune: John Harper.

Text and first tune: © 1995, Mount Saint Bernard Abbey, Coalville, Leicester LE67 5UL. Second tune:
© 1995, Panel of Monastic Musicians, Mount Saint Bernard Abbey, Coalville, Leicester LE67 5UL.

157   10.10.10.10

First tune   TINTERN   *Mode 8: G*

E - gypt is far be - hind, the Red Sea crossed,

And new - ly clothed in robes of gleam - ing white

We come to share the sup - per of the Lamb,

And sing to Christ, our shep - herd and our king.

Text: Mount Saint Bernard Abbey, altered; from *Ad cenam agni providi*, Saint Niceta of Remesiana (d. c. 414). First tune: Mount Saint Bernard Abbey.

Text and first tune: © 1995, Mount Saint Bernard Abbey, Coalville, Leicester LE67 5UL.

EASTER

1   Egypt is far behind, the Red Sea crossed,
     And newly clothed in robes of gleaming white
     We come to share the supper of the Lamb,
     And sing to Christ, our shepherd and our king.

2   Burnt on the altar of the cross for us,
     His body there became our daily food:
     We drink the blood poured out on our behalf,
     And by that food we live our life in God.

3   Signed with the saving blood we stand secure,
     While God's avenging angel passes by;
     From Pharaoh's galling yoke set free at last
     We eat the paschal Lamb with joyous hearts.

4   Christ is the paschal Lamb we eat today,
     Whose sacrifice fulfils the ancient rite:
     Unleavened bread of faithfulness and truth
     Is now the offering of his flesh and blood.

5   Worthy the victim for so great an act:
     The powers of hell lie broken in their pride,
     The people once in bondage now goes free,
     And life returns where death had ruled supreme.

6   Christ with the dawn arises from the tomb,
     A victor, he returns from death's domain,
     He binds the evil one with chains of bronze,
     And opens wide the gates of Paradise.

7   Maker of all, we beg of you to grant
     That during this our joyful paschal time
     You guard from every sickness and from death
     The people that your Son has now redeemed.

8   Glory is yours, O Christ our Lord and God,
     Arisen from the dead to be our life,
     With Father and the Holy Spirit one
     From age to age beyond the bounds of time.

157

10.10.10.10

Second tune

MAGDA

Text: Mount Saint Bernard Abbey, altered; from *Ad cenam agni providi*, Saint Niceta of Remesiana (d. c. 414). Second tune: Ralph Vaughan Williams (1872-1958), from *Enlarged Songs of Praise, 1931*.

Text: © 1995, Mount Saint Bernard Abbey, Coalville, Leicester LE67 5UL. Second tune: © Oxford University Press.

EASTER

1　Egypt is far behind, the Red Sea crossed,
　And newly clothed in robes of gleaming white
　We come to share the supper of the Lamb,
　And sing to Christ, our shepherd and our king.

2　Burnt on the altar of the cross for us,
　His body there became our daily food:
　We drink the blood poured out on our behalf,
　And by that food we live our life in God.

3　Signed with the saving blood we stand secure,
　While God's avenging angel passes by;
　From Pharaoh's galling yoke set free at last
　We eat the paschal Lamb with joyous hearts.

4　Christ is the paschal Lamb we eat today,
　Whose sacrifice fulfils the ancient rite:
　Unleavened bread of faithfulness and truth
　Is now the offering of his flesh and blood.

5　Worthy the victim for so great an act:
　The powers of hell lie broken in their pride,
　The people once in bondage now goes free,
　And life returns where death had ruled supreme.

6　Christ with the dawn arises from the tomb,
　A victor, he returns from death's domain,
　He binds the evil one with chains of bronze,
　And opens wide the gates of Paradise.

7　Maker of all, we beg of you to grant
　That during this our joyful paschal time
　You guard from every sickness and from death
　The people that your Son has now redeemed.

8　Glory is yours, O Christ our Lord and God,
　Arisen from the dead to be our life,
　With Father and the Holy Spirit one
　From age to age beyond the bounds of time.

158

LM

First tune AURORA LUCIS RUTILAT (i) *Mode 8: F*

Pro - claim his tri - umph, heaven and earth,

For Christ is ri - sen as he said:

The cru - ci - fied, the liv - ing God,

Who dwelt three days a - mong the dead.

Second tune SOLEMNIS HAEC FESTIVITAS

EASTER

1   Proclaim his triumph, heaven and earth,
For Christ is risen as he said:
The crucified, the living God,
Who dwelt three days among the dead.

2   He broke apart the gates of hell,
Freed waiting Adam from his chain;
And in the radiance of the Lord
The face of Moses shone again.

3   Christ died for us in bitter shame,
But now he lives in power and might:
His fire unquenched, his vital flame
Fills all the world with joy and light.

4   The uncreated Father praise,
His living and unconquered Son,
Who with the Spirit reign supreme,
Triumphant Trinity in One.

Text: Stanbrook Abbey. Second tune: melody, Paris Gradual, 1685; harmony, John Harper.

Text: © 1974, Stanbrook Abbey, Callow End, Worcester WR2 4TD. Second tune (harmony): © 1995, Panel of Monastic Musicians, Mount Saint Bernard Abbey, Coalville, Leicester LE67 5UL.

159

Irregular

First tune   **LLANFAES**   *Mode 2: A*

1 Stay with us Lord   for   day ___   is   al - most o - ver,
2 Stay with us Lord,   your   word ___   like fire with - in   us
3 Stay with us Lord,   and   e - ver go   be - fore us,

Come to   us   in   peace _   and greet us   with your word;
Sheds its search - ing light ___ on   all ___   our   de - spair:
Soon ___ will your fu - ture dawn on   us   like day;

You we have known, ___ your ___ love has sought and found us,
We   had for - got - ten ___ you, the   ri - sen Mas - ter,
Stretch out your hand __ to ___ hold and lead us al - ways,

Speak to   us   now, ___ our   bro - ther and our Lord.
Tak - ing   our   way, ___ you   talked __ with us   there.
Gen - tle and strong __ one, Lord ___ of   our way.

EASTER

1   Stay with us Lord, for day is almost over;
    Come to us in peace and greet us with your word.
    You we have known, your love has sought and found us:
    Speak to us now, our brother and our Lord.

2   Stay with us Lord, your word like fire within us
    Sheds its searching light on all our despair:
    We had forgotten you, the risen Master,
    Taking our way, you talked with us there.

3   Stay with us Lord, and ever go before us,
    Soon will your future dawn on us like day;
    Stretch out your hand to hold and lead us always,
    Gentle and strong one, Lord of our way.

Text: Alan Griffiths. First tune: John Harper.

Text: © 1995, Alan Griffiths. First tune: © 1995, Panel of Monastic Musicians, Mount Saint Bernard
Abbey, Coalville, Leicester LE67 5UL.

159

Second tune   PEREGRINUS

1. Stay with us Lord, for day is al-most o-ver,
2. Stay with us Lord, your word like fire with-in us
3. Stay with us Lord, and e-ver go be-fore us,

Come to us in peace and greet us with your word;
Sheds its search-ing light on all __ our des-pair:
Soon __ will your fu-ture dawn on us like day;

You we have known, your love has sought and found us,
We had for-got-ten you, the ri-sen Mas-ter,
Stretch out your hand to hold and lead us al-ways,

Speak to us now, — our bro-ther and our Lord.
Tak-ing our way, — you talked — with us there.
Gen-tle and strong — one, Lord — of our way.

Text: Alan Griffiths. Second tune: John Harper.

Text: © 1995, Alan Griffiths. Second tune: © 1995, Panel of Monastic Musicians, Mount Saint Bernard Abbey, Coalville, Leicester LE67 5UL.

160
7.7.7.4

First tune   **CHRISTUS RESURREXIT**   *Mode 1: D*

Christ the Lord is ris'n a - gain; Christ has bro - ken ev' - ry chain;

Hark, the an-gels shout for joy, Sing-ing ev-er-more on high, Al-le - lu - ia.

Al - le – lu – ia. Al - le – lu – ia. Al - le – lu – ia.

Second tune   **WURTEMBURG**

Al – le – lu – ia.

Alternative: ORIENTIS PARTIBUS, 118

EASTER

1   Christ the Lord is risen again;
     Christ has broken every chain;
     Hark, the angels shout for joy,
     Singing evermore on high,
     Alleluia.

2   He who gave for us his life,
     Who for us endured the strife,
     Is our paschal Lamb today;
     We too sing for joy, and say
     Alleluia.

3   He who bore all pain and loss
     Comfortless upon the cross,
     Lives in glory now on high,
     Pleads for us, and hears our cry.
     Alleluia.

4   Now he bids us tell abroad
     How the lost may be restored,
     How the penitent forgiven,
     How we too may enter heaven.
     Alleluia.

Text: Catherine Winkworth (1829-78), abbreviated and altered; from *Christus ist erstanden*, Michael Weisse (c. 1480-1534). First tune: 12th century. Second tune: adapted from *Hundert Arien*, Dresden 1694, by William H. Monk (1823-89).

161 10.9.10.9

First tune **HILDELITH** *Mode 2: G*

Who is this who comes to us in tri - umph,

Clothed in roy - al gar - ments dyed with blood,

Walk - ing in the great - ness of his glo - ry,

Bear - ing in his hand the ho - ly rood?

Second tune **LLANGOED**

EASTER

1   Who is this who comes to us in triumph,
        Clothed in royal garments dyed with blood,
        Walking in the greatness of his glory,
        Bearing in his hand the holy rood?

2   This is Christ the risen Lord, the strong one,
        He who trod the winepress all alone:
        Out of death he comes with life unending,
        Seeking those he purchased for his own.

3   Wonderful and great is our redeemer,
        Christ the living one, the just and true:
        Praise him with the Father and the Spirit,
        Ever with us, making all things new.

Text: Stanbrook Abbey. First tune: Stanbrook Abbey. Second tune: John Harper.

Text and first tune: © 1974, Stanbrook Abbey, Callow End, Worcester WR2 4TD. Second tune: © 1995, Panel of Monastic Musicians, Mount Saint Bernard Abbey, Coalville, Leicester LE67 5UL.

162   7.7.7.7

First tune   ALS CHRISTUS MIT SEINER LEHR   *Mode 1: D*

Eas - ter glo - ry fills the sky: Christ now lives, no more to die.

Dark-ness has been put to flight By the liv - ing Lord of light.

Second tune   GOTT SEI DANK (LUBECK)

Alternatives: ORIENTIS PARTIBUS, 118; WÜRTEMBURG, 160

EASTER

1   Easter glory fills the sky:
Christ now lives, no more to die.
Darkness has been put to flight
By the living Lord of light.

2   Mary, mother, greet your Son,
Radiant from his triumph won;
By his cross you shared his pain,
So for ever share his reign.

3   Shepherd, seek the sheep that strayed,
Come to contrite Peter's aid.
Strengthen him to be the rock;
Make him shepherd of your flock.

4   Seek not life within the tomb:
Christ stands in the upper room.
Risen glory he conceals,
Risen body he reveals.

5   Though we see his face no more,
He is with us as before.
Glory veiled, he is our priest,
His true flesh and blood our feast.

Text: James Quinn SJ, abbreviated. First tune: Bohemian Brothers (1566). Second tune: melody adapted from J. A. Freylinghausen, *Geistreiches Gesangbuch*, Halle 1704; harmony, William H. Havergal (1793-1870) and William H. Monk (1823-89).

163 CM

First tune   VICTIMAE PASCHALI   *Mode 1: D*

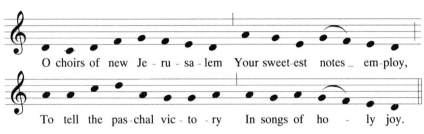

O choirs of new Je - ru - sa - lem Your sweet-est notes _ em-ploy,

To tell the pas-chal vic - to - ry In songs of ho - ly joy.

Second tune   SAINT FULBERT

EASTER

1   O choirs of new Jerusalem
     Your sweetest notes employ,
     To tell the paschal victory
     In songs of holy joy.

2   How Judah's lion burst his chains,
     And crushed the serpent's head,
     And brought with him, from death's domains,
     The long-imprisoned dead.

3   The depths of hell their captive prey
     Release to life once more;
     This ransomed host pursues the way
     Where Christ is gone before.

4   Triumphant in his glory now,
     To him all power is given;
     To him does every creature bow:
     Christ reigns on high in heaven.

5   While joyful thus his praise we sing,
     His mercy we implore,
     Into his palace bright to bring
     And keep us evermore.

6   All glory, Lord, your people give,
     To Christ the risen Son,
     That in your Spirit we may live,
     And praise you, ever one.

Text: Robert Campbell (1814-68), altered; from *Chorus novae Ierusalem,* Saint Fulbert of Chartres (d. 1028). First tune: Alan Rees OSB, adapted from *Victimae paschali laudes.* Second tune: Henry J. Gauntlett (1805-76).

164

7.5.7.4

BEAULIEU

Mode 4: A

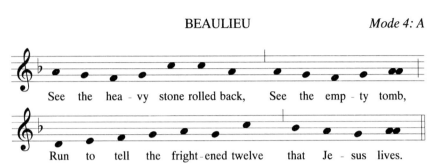

See the hea - vy stone rolled back, See the emp - ty tomb,

Run to tell the fright - ened twelve that Je - sus lives.

EASTER

1   See the heavy stone rolled back,
     See the empty tomb,
     Run to tell the frightened twelve
     That Jesus lives.

2   Kneel before his wounded feet,
     Touch his hands and side,
     Leave your doubting and believe
     The Son of Man.

3   Cloud that led the chosen race,
     Fire that burned by night,
     Glory of the Triune God
     In Jesus' face.

Text and tune: Mount Saint Bernard Abbey.

Text and tune: © 1995, Mount Saint Bernard Abbey, Coalville, Leicester LE67 5UL.

165   SM

First tune   SURREXIT VERE   *Mode 7: E*

The Lord is ris'n in - deed; Now is his work _ per-formed;

Now is the migh-ty cap-tive freed, And death's strong ca - stle stormed.

Second tune   NARENZA

EASTER

1   The Lord is risen indeed;
       Now is his work performed;
       Now is the mighty captive freed,
       And death's strong castle stormed.

2   The Lord is risen indeed;
       Then hell has lost his prey;
       With him is risen the ransomed seed
       To reign in endless day.

3   The Lord is risen indeed;
       He lives, to die no more;
       He lives, the sinner's cause to plead,
       Whose curse and shame he bore.

Text: Thomas Kelly (1769-1844). First tune: Alan Rees OSB. Second tune: melody adapted from Leisentritt, *Catholicum Hymnologium Germanicum*, Bautzen 1584; harmony, William H. Havergal (1793-1870).

First tune: © 1995, Belmont Abbey Trustees, Hereford, HR2 9RZ.

166   CM

First tune   KIDWELLY   *Mode 1: D*

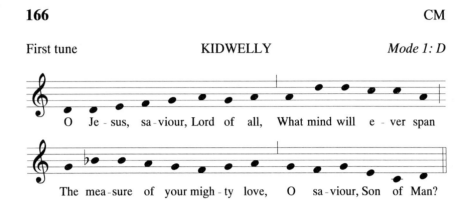

O Je - sus, sa - viour, Lord of all, What mind will e - ver span

The mea - sure of your migh - ty love, O sa - viour, Son of Man?

Second tune   SAINT MAGNUS

ASCENSION

1   O Jesus, saviour, Lord of all,
      What mind will ever span
      The measure of your mighty love,
      O saviour, Son of Man?

2   What loving mercy held your heart
      That you should bear our sin?
      Should let yourself be crushed by death
      That our life might begin?

3   You broke the power of sin and death,
      You tore the gateway wide;
      And all who welcomed you were led
      Back to the Father's side.

4   May this same love surround us now
      To free us from all harm,
      That we may soon meet face to face
      Within our Father's home.

5   O Jesus, be our joy this day,
      Our comfort in this place;
      May this your risen life be ours
      That we may know your peace.

Text: Ralph Wright OSB; from *Iesu, nostra redemptio* (7th or 8th century). First tune: Alan Rees OSB. Second tune: Jeremiah Clarke (c. 1674-1707).

167

LM

First tune   IESU, REDEMPTOR SAECULI   *Mode 1: E*

King of all a - ges, throned on ____ high,

Yet sa - viour too ____ of those with faith,

Death at your on - slaught died in fear ____

And grace tri - umph - ant rules ____ su - preme.

Second tune   SONG 34

ASCENSION

1   King of all ages, throned on high,
    Yet saviour too of those with faith,
    Death at your onslaught died in fear
    And grace triumphant rules supreme.

2   Risen from death, the heavenly Christ
    Receives from God the Father's hand
    Power over all created things:
    A gift he could not know on earth.

3   Grant us to find our joy in you,
    Possess you in our heavenly home,
    King of this passing world of time,
    And source of truth and lasting joy.

4   Then, at your coming on the clouds
    With shining strength to be our judge,
    Cancel the debt we owe you still,
    Give back the glory we have lost.

5   Glory to you, O Christ our Lord,
    Exalted far beyond our sight,
    Reigning in bliss for evermore,
    With Father and with Paraclete.

Text: Mount Saint Bernard Abbey, abbreviated; from *Aeterne rex altissime* (10th century). Second tune: melody and bass, Orlando Gibbons (1583-1625).

Text: © 1995, Mount Saint Bernard Abbey, Coalville, Leicester LE67 5UL.

168 LM

First tune　　　　AURORA LUCIS RUTILAT (ii)　　　　*Mode 7: E*

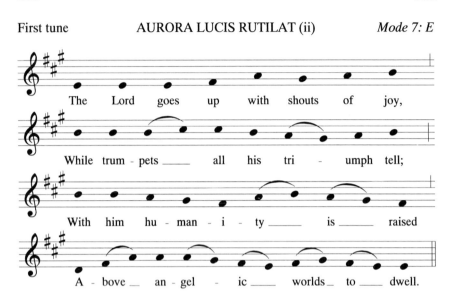

The Lord goes up with shouts of joy,

While trum - pets ___ all his tri - umph tell;

With him hu - man - i - ty ___ is ___ raised

A - bove ___ an - gel - ic ___ worlds ___ to ___ dwell.

Second tune　　O AMOR QUAM EXSTATICUS (RESURREXIT)

ASCENSION

1   The Lord goes up with shouts of joy,
    While trumpets all his triumph tell;
    With him humanity is raised
    Above angelic worlds to dwell.

2   He sits with God, at his right hand,
    Who is the Lord of everything:
    The Father's glory is his own;
    Christ Jesus, all creation's king.

3   And when he comes again in might
    To raise us on that splendid day,
    We shall be gathered up to him,
    And every tear be wiped away.

4   O God, our Father, hear our prayer:
    With Christ, our Lord, your only Son,
    Send forth the Spirit of your love
    To live in us and make us one.

Text: Stanbrook Abbey. Second tune: French church melody; harmony, Ralph Vaughan Williams (1872-1958), from *The English Hymnal*, altered.

169   LM

First tune   IESU, REDEMPTOR SAECULI   *Mode 1: E*

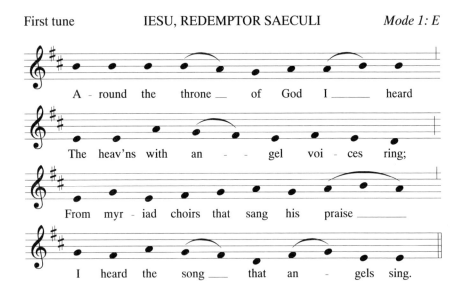

A - round the throne __ of God I ____ heard

The heav'ns with an - gel voi - ces ring;

From myr - iad choirs that sang his praise ____

I heard the song __ that an - gels sing.

1   Around the throne of God I heard
The heavens with angel voices ring;
From myriad choirs that sang his praise
I heard the song that angels sing.

2   'To Christ the Lamb that that once was slain,
All kingship, riches, wisdom, might,
All honour, glory, blessing be,
For all is his by sovereign right.'

3   All living things in heaven above,
All living things of earth and sea,
Took up the song the angels sang,
And echoed back their minstrelsy.

4   'All blessing, honour, glory, power,
For evermore to God be given,
And equal praise to Christ the Lamb,
Enthroned with him in highest heaven.'

5   So now with angels round the throne,
With every living creature, raise
To God and God's victorious Lamb
The Alleluia of your praise.

Second tune BRESLAU

Alternative: Father, Lord of earth and heaven, 175.

Text: James Quinn SJ; based on Revelation 5, 11-13. Second tune: melody, *Locheimer Gesangbuch*, 15th century, as in C. Gall, *As Hymnodus Sacer*, Leipzig 1625; harmony derived from Felix Mendelssohn (1809-47).

170   LM

First tune   VENI, CREATOR SPIRITUS   *Mode 8: F*

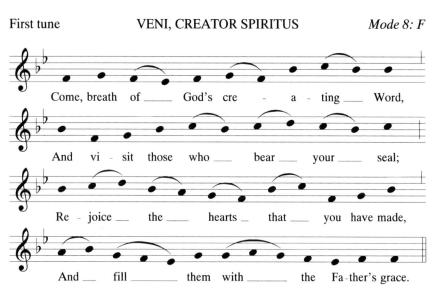

Come, breath of ___ God's cre - a - ting ___ Word,

And vi - sit those who ___ bear ___ your ___ seal;

Re - joice ___ the ___ hearts ___ that ___ you have made,

And ___ fill ___ them with ___ the Fa - ther's grace.

Second tune   FINNART

Alternative: DEO GRACIAS, 171

PENTECOST

170

1   Come, breath of God's creating Word,
    And visit those who bear your seal;
    Rejoice the hearts that you have made,
    And fill them with the Father's grace.

2   We turn to you, our advocate,
    The uncreated gift of God,
    The living water, flame of love,
    Who consecrates us to the Son.

3   You are yourself the sevenfold gift,
    The finger of our God's right hand,
    The Father's promised advocate,
    Enriching us with words of praise.

4   Shine from within through every sense,
    And pour your love into our hearts;
    Make strong the weakness of our flesh
    With your unfailing, timeless power.

5   Drive Satan headlong from our midst,
    And bring us true and lasting peace;
    Go on before to show the way,
    And keep us from all paths of sin.

6   Grant us by your own gifts to know
    The Father and his only Son;
    And may we trust you all our days,
    O ever-present Spirit-breath.

7   All glory to our God and Lord,
    And to his Son who conquered death;
    All glory to the Paraclete,
    Who reigns with them eternally.

Text: Mount Saint Bernard Abbey, altered; from *Veni, creator Spiritus*, Rabanus Maurus (776-856).
Second tune: Kenneth Finlay (1882-1974).

Text: © 1995, Mount Saint Bernard Abbey, Coalville, Leicester LE67 5UL. Second tune: © 1986,
executors of Kenneth Finlay.

171 LM

First tune VENI, CREATOR SPIRITUS *Mode 8: F*

Cre - a - tor ___ Spi - rit ___ from on ___ high,

De - scend and fill our ___ minds __ with ___ light,

Breathe on ___ the ___ souls __ whom _ you have formed

With _ your ___ cre - a - - tive breath of love.

1   Creator Spirit from on high,
Descend and fill our minds with light.
Breathe on the souls whom you have formed
With your creative breath of love.

2   Come, strengthener and advocate,
Awaited gift of God most high,
The springing well, the fount of life,
The soul's anointing fire of love.

3   With sevenfold endowment, come,
The guiding finger of our God,
The Father's promised Paraclete,
Inspire our lips to speak your word.

4   Set every sense on fire with light,
Pour forth your love to fill our hearts,
The weakness of our mortal flesh
Uphold with your eternal power.

5   Drive far away our ancient foe,
Give evermore your gift of peace,
And go before, that taught of you
All touch of evil we may shun.

Second tune   DEO GRACIAS (AGINCOURT)

Alternative: FINNART, 170

6   True knowledge of the Father bring,
       True knowledge of his only Son,
       And you, O Spirit, one with them,
       May we confess with steadfast faith.

Text: Saint Mary's Abbey, West Malling; from *Veni, creator Spiritus*, Rabanus Maurus (776-856). Second tune: melody, 15th-century English; harmony, John Harper.

172   10.10.10.10

First tune   **VERBUM DEI**   *Mode 8: G*

Love of the Father, Love of God the Son,
From whom all came, in whom all was begun;
Who formest heavenly beauty out of strife,
Creation's whole desire and breath of life.

1   Love of the Father, Love of God the Son,
     From whom all came, in whom all was begun;
     Who formest heavenly beauty out of strife,
     Creation's whole desire and breath of life.

2   Thou art all-holy, thou supreme in might,
     Thou dost give peace, thy presence maketh right;
     Thou with thy favour all things dost enfold,
     With thine all-kindness free from harm wilt hold.

3   Purest and highest, wisest and most just,
     There is no truth save only in thy trust;
     Thou dost the mind from earthly dreams recall,
     And bring, through Christ, to him for whom are all.

4   Glory eternal, thee do we adore,
     Who art and shall be worshipped evermore:
     Us whom thou madest, comfort with thy might,
     And lead us to enjoy thy heavenly light.

Text: Robert Bridges (1844-1930), altered; from *Amor Patris et Filii* (12th century). First tune: editors, adapted from *Verbum supernum prodiens nec Patris*. Second tune: melody and bass, Orlando Gibbons (1583-1625).

PENTECOST

EVENING PRAYER

Second tune SONG 22

First tune: © 1995, Panel of Monastic Musicians, Mount Saint Bernard Abbey, Coalville, Leicester LE67 5UL.

173 7.7.7.7

First tune   PORINGLAND   *Mode 1: F♯*

Spi - rit of the Lord, come down, Spread-ing your pro - tec -tive wing

O - ver all that you have made, O - ver ev'- ry liv – ing thing.

Second tune   SONG 13

PENTECOST

1   Spirit of the Lord, come down,
       Spreading your protective wing
       Over all that you have made,
       Over every living thing.

2   Come in storm-wind, cleansing fire,
       Sweeping through a world unclean;
       Come in every gentle breeze:
       Breath of God, unheard, unseen.

3   Holy Spirit, blessed Light,
       Guide and strengthen mind and will;
       Comfort every grieving heart,
       And our inmost being fill.

4   Through the Father and the Son,
       By whose blood our life was bought,
       Fill our empty hands with gifts:
       Come with grace unearned, unsought.

Text: Stanbrook Abbey. First tune: James Walsh OSB. Second tune: melody and bass from Orlando Gibbons (1583-1625).

Text: © 1974, Stanbrook Abbey, Callow End, Worcester WR2 4TD. First tune: © 1976, James Walsh OSB.

174

LM

First tune   VENI, REDEMPTOR GENTIUM (ii)   *Mode 2: F*

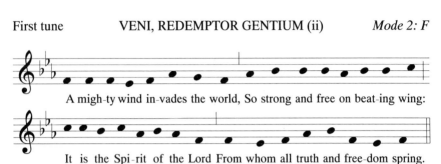

A migh-ty wind in-vades the world, So strong and free on beat-ing wing:

It is the Spi-rit of the Lord From whom all truth and free-dom spring.

Alternative: IESU, REDEMPTOR SAECULI, 167

Second tune   PATRI MONSTRAT

PENTECOST

1   A mighty wind invades the world,
So strong and free on beating wing:
It is the Spirit of the Lord
From whom all truth and freedom spring.

2   The Spirit is a fountain clear
For ever leaping to the sky,
Whose waters give unending life,
Whose timeless source is never dry.

3   The Spirit comes in tongues of flame,
With love and wisdom burning bright:
The wind, the fountain and the fire
Combine in this great feast of light.

4   O tranquil Spirit, bring us peace,
With God the Father and the Son.
We praise you, blessed Trinity,
Unchanging, and for ever one.

Text: Stanbrook Abbey. Second tune: melody, La Feillée, *Méthode du Plain-chant*, 1752; harmony, John Harper.

Text: © 1974, Stanbrook Abbey, Callow End, Worcester WR2 4TD. Second tune (harmony): © 1995, Panel of Monastic Musicians, Mount Saint Bernard Abbey, Coalville, Leicester LE67 5UL.

175

8.7.8.7

First tune   PER ORBEM   *Mode 2: G*

Fa-ther, Lord of earth and hea-ven, King to whom all gifts be-long,

Give your great-est gift, your Spi-rit, God the ho-ly, God the strong.

Second tune   SUSSEX

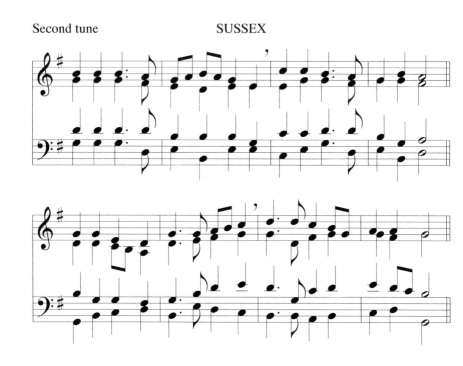

PENTECOST

1   Father, Lord of earth and heaven,
    King to whom all gifts belong,
    Give your greatest gift, your Spirit,
    God the holy, God the strong.

2   Son of God, enthroned in glory,
    Send your promised gift of grace;
    Make your Church your holy temple,
    God the Spirit's dwelling-place.

3   Spirit, come in peace descending
    As at Jordan, heavenly dove;
    Seal your Church as God's anointed,
    Set our hearts on fire with love.

Text: James Quinn SJ. First tune: second strain of sequence, *Sponsa Christi*, Grenoble 17th century. Second tune: English traditional melody, adapted and arranged by Ralph Vaughan Williams (1872-1958), from *The English Hymnal*.

176 6.6.8.4

First tune PARACLETE *Mode d: A*

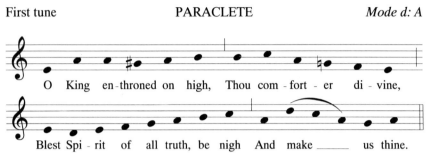

O King en-throned on high, Thou com-fort-er di-vine,

Blest Spi-rit of all truth, be nigh And make us thine.

Second tune TEMPLE

PENTECOST

1   O King enthroned on high,
    Thou comforter divine,
    Blest Spirit of all truth, be nigh
    And make us thine.

2   Thou art the source of life,
    Thou art our treasure-store;
    Give us thy peace, and end our strife
    For evermore.

3   Descend, O heavenly dove,
    Abide with us alway;
    And in the fullness of thy love
    Cleanse us, we pray.

Text: John Brownlie (1857-1925); from the Greek (8th century). First tune: Alan Rees OSB. Second tune: H. Walford Davies (1869-1941).

First tune: © 1995, Belmont Abbey Trustees, Hereford, HR2 9RZ. Second tune: © Oxford University Press.

177   9.8.9.8

First tune   CALDEY   *Mode 1: D*

O breath of life, come sweep - ing through us,

Re - vive your Church with life and power;

O breath of life, come cleanse re - new us,

And fit your Church to meet this hour.

Second tune   LES DIX COMMANDEMENS

PENTECOST

1   O breath of life, come sweeping through us,
      Revive your Church with life and power;
      O breath of life, come cleanse, renew us,
      And fit your Church to meet this hour.

2   O breath of God, come bend us, break us,
      Till humbly we confess our need;
      Then in your tenderness remake us,
      Revive, restore: for this we plead.

3   O breath of love, come breathe within us,
      Renewing thought and will and heart;
      Come, love of Christ, afresh to win us,
      Revive your Church in every part.

Text: Bessie Porter Head (1850-1936). First tune: Charles Watson OSB. Second tune: composed or adapted by Louis Bourgeois (c. 1510-61).

First tune: © 1995, Charles Watson OSB, Prinknash Abbey, Cranham, Gloucester GL4 8EX.

178

LM

First tune   O LUX, BEATA TRINITAS   *Mode 8: G*

Be _ with us ho-ly Tri - ni-ty, Three _ per - sons like in ma - jes-ty,

One on-ly_ God sus - tain - ing _ all, Cre-a - tor, sa-viour, com - fort-er.

Second tune   SOLOTHURN

HOLY TRINITY

1   Be with us holy Trinity,
Three persons like in majesty,
One only God sustaining all,
Creator, saviour, comforter.

2   The hosts of angels worship you,
Adore you, and proclaim you Lord;
And all creation's power unite
To bless your name from age to age.

3   In supplication here we kneel,
Your worshippers, with love and awe,
Repeating in our humbler prayers
The praises of the heavenly choir.

4   With all things living we adore
The Alpha and the Omega,
And celebrate in threefold name,
The glory of the one true light.

5   All praise to you, blest Trinity,
To Father and incarnate Word,
Both with the Holy Spirit, one
For time and all eternity.

Text: editors' compilation; from *Adesto, sancta Trinitas* (10th or 11th century). Second tune: melody, Swiss traditional; harmony, Ralph Vaughan Williams (1872-1958), from *The English Hymnal*, altered.

Text (this version): © 1995, Panel of Monastic Musicians, Mount Saint Bernard Abbey, Coalville, Leicester LE67 5UL. Second tune (harmony): © Oxford University Press. Altered by permission.

179   11.11.11.5

First tune   O PATER SANCTE   *Mode 4: E*

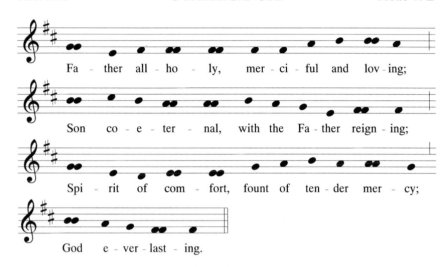

Fa – ther all – ho – ly,   mer – ci – ful and   lov – ing;

Son   co – e – ter – nal,   with the   Fa – ther   reign – ing;

Spi – rit of   com – fort,   fount of   ten – der   mer – cy;

God   e – ver – last – ing.

1   Father all-holy, merciful and loving;
     Son co-eternal, with the Father reigning;
     Spirit of comfort, fount of tender mercy;
     God everlasting.

2   All your works praise you, all your saints extol you;
     They for your pleasure are and were created.
     Now while we also worship and adore you
     Hear our glad voices.

3   Yours be the glory, Trinity all-holy,
     One in three persons, reigning in the highest;
     Glory and honour, song and praise befit you,
     Now and for ever.

HOLY TRINITY

Second tune   HERR, DEINEN ZORN

Text: Saint Mary's Abbey, West Malling; from *O Pater sancte* (c. 10th century). Second tune: melody adapted from Johann Crüger (1598-1662); harmony, Richard Dubois, altered.

Text: © 1995, Saint Mary's Abbey, West Malling, Kent ME19 6JX. Second tune (harmony): © 1972, Richard Dubois; by permission of Paul Inwood.

180

LM

First tune

BENEDICT

Mode 1: D

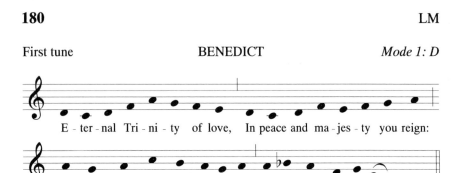

E - ter - nal Tri - ni - ty of love, In peace and ma - jes - ty you reign:

All things come forth from you a-lone; To you they must re-turn _ a-gain.

Second tune

SONG 34

HOLY TRINITY

1   Eternal Trinity of love,
     In peace and majesty you reign:
     All things come forth from you alone;
     To you they must return again.

2   Creation lives and breathes in you,
     Sustained by your almighty will;
     Grant us to know you, God of truth,
     In whom the questing mind is still.

3   Our Father, in the name of Christ,
     Unceasingly your Spirit send;
     Be with us, everlasting God:
     Fulfil your purpose to the end.

4   We praise you, Godhead, One in Three,
     Immortal Trinity of light,
     Unchanging through eternal days
     You live unmoved, serene in might.

Text: Stanbrook Abbey. First tune: Anthony Greening. Second tune: melody and bass, Orlando Gibbons (1583-1625).

Text: © 1974, Stanbrook Abbey, Callow End, Worcester WR2 4TD. First tune: © 1995, Elmore Abbey, Church Lane, Speen, Newbury, Berkshire RG13 1SA; by permission of the abbot and community.

181   8.7.8.7.8.7

First tune   PANGE LINGUA GLORIOSI (i)   *Mode 3: E*

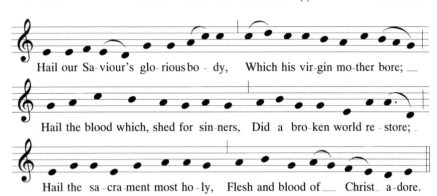

Hail our Sa-viour's glo-rious bo - dy,   Which his vir-gin mo-ther bore; —

Hail the blood which, shed for sin-ners,   Did a bro-ken world re - store; —

Hail the sa - cra-ment most ho - ly,   Flesh and blood of __ Christ __ a-dore.

Alternative: PANGE LINGUA GLORIOSI (ii), 149

1 Hail our Saviour's glorious body,
  Which his virgin mother bore;
  Hail the blood which, shed for sinners,
  Did a broken world restore;
  Hail the sacrament most holy,
  Flesh and blood of Christ adore.

2 To the Virgin, for our healing,
  His own Son the Father sends;
  From the Father's love proceeding
  Sower, seed and Word descends:
  Wondrous life of Word incarnate
  With his greatest wonder ends.

3 On the paschal evening see him
  With the chosen twelve recline,
  To the old law still obedient
  In its feast of love divine;
  Love divine, the new law giving,
  Gives himself as bread and wine.

4 By his word the Word almighty
  Makes of bread his flesh indeed;
  Wine becomes his very life-blood:
  Faith God's living Word must heed.
  Faith alone may safely guide us
  Where the senses cannot lead.

5 Come, adore this wondrous presence;
  Bow to Christ, the source of grace:
  Here is kept the ancient promise
  Of God's earthly dwelling-place.
  Sight is blind before God's glory,
  Faith alone may see his face.

6 Glory be to God the Father,
  Praise to his co-equal Son,
  Adoration to the Spirit,
  Bond of love, in Godhead one;
  Blest be God by all creation
  Joyously while ages run.

THE BODY OF CHRIST

Second tune   ORIEL

Alternatives: FORTUNATUS NEW, 148; TANTUM ERGO, 149

Text: James Quinn SJ, altered; from *Pange lingua gloriosi corporis*, Saint Thomas Aquinas? (1227-74).
Second tune: C. Ett, *Cantica Sacra*, Munich 1840.

182

First tune CHRISTE, QUI SPLENDOR ET DIES (ii) *Mode 8: F*

Christ gives his child-ren an-gels' food, His bo-dy and his blood_ di-vine;

The poor re-ceive a price-less gift:_ Strong bread of life,_ im-mor-tal_ life.

Second tune   O SALUTARIS

THE BODY OF CHRIST

1   Christ gives his children angels' food,
     His body and his blood divine;
     The poor receive a priceless gift:
     Strong bread of life, immortal wine.

2   There is no other bread than this
     By which the hungry can be filled;
     No other wine has hidden power
     Whereby the spirit's thirst is stilled.

3   All those who have believed his word,
     And share, in love, this holy bread,
     Who drink together from his cup,
     Christ will not leave among the dead.

4   To all rejoicing at this feast
     Death opens doors on realms of light
     Where Father, Son and Spirit reign,
     And we attain immortal life.

Text: Stanbrook Abbey. Second tune: Abbé Duguet, c. 1767.

Text: © 1974 and 1995, Stanbrook Abbey, Callow End, Worcester WR2 4TD.

183

LM

First tune   VERBUM SUPERNUM PRODIENS   *Mode 8: G*

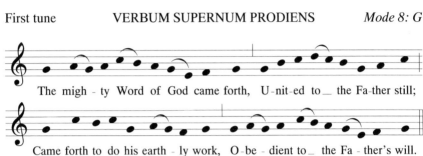

The migh - ty Word of God came forth, U-nit-ed to _ the Fa-ther still;

Came forth to do his earth - ly work, O-be - dient to _ the Fa - ther's will.

Second tune   AUCTORITATE SAECULI

THE BODY OF CHRIST

183

1   The mighty Word of God came forth,
     United to the Father still;
     Came forth to do his earthly work,
     Obedient to the Father's will.

2   The night when he was given to death
     He gave his body to his friends;
     In living and life-giving bread
     The saviour of the world descends.

3   He gives to us in twofold kind
     His sacred body and his blood;
     Our twofold self receives from him
     The body and the spirit's food.

4   Our friend and brother he was born,
     Whose death redeemed us on the tree;
     He reigns for ever, God supreme,
     Our prize for all eternity.

5   O victim sacrificed for all,
     Give strength against the foe within;
     Throw open your eternal gates,
     That we, your own, may enter in.

6   Blest Trinity, we give you praise,
     Whose mighty power all things transcends;
     Bring us to where your glory dwells,
     And grant us life that never ends.

Text: Stanbrook Abbey; from *Verbum supernum prodiens nec Patris*, Saint Thomas Aquinas (1227-84). First tune: *Antiphonarium Romanum*, Mechlin 1838. Second tune: melody: Poitiers Antiphoner, 1746; harmony, editors.

Text: © 1974 and 1995, Stanbrook Abbey, Callow End, Worcester WR2 4TD. Second tune (harmony): © Panel of Monastic Musicians, Mount Saint Bernard Abbey, Coalville, Leicester LE67 5UL.

184

8.9.8.9

WHITLAND

Mode 8: F

Word and wis - dom of the Fa - ther,

An - cient pro - phets longed to see your day:

You a - lone re - veal the king - dom,

Bring - ing light where dark - ness once ___ pre - vailed.

THE SACRED HEART OF JESUS

1   Word and wisdom of the Father,
    Ancient prophets longed to see your day:
    You alone reveal the kingdom,
    Bringing light where darkness once prevailed.

2   Jesus, saviour, son of David,
    Prince of Judah, rule our wayward hearts;
    Shepherd of God's holy people,
    Guide our steps in ways of peace and love.

3   Aaron's priestly rites foreshadowed
    Your surpassing sacrifice of praise:
    Flesh and blood, your one oblation,
    Offered up for all on Calvary hill.

4   Lamb of God, so rich in mercy,
    Blood and water from your wounded heart
    Washed away our sins and healed us:
    Never love so great was known on earth.

5   Lord, whose heart is meek and lowly,
    Praise we sing and honour to your name;
    Praise and honour to the Father,
    With the Spirit, one eternal God.

Text : Mount Saint Bernard Abbey, altered. Tune: Mount Saint Bernard Abbey.

Text and tune: © 1995, Mount Saint Bernard Abbey, Coalville, Leicester LE67 5UL.

185

LM

First tune   IESU, REX ADMIRABILIS   *Mode d: D*

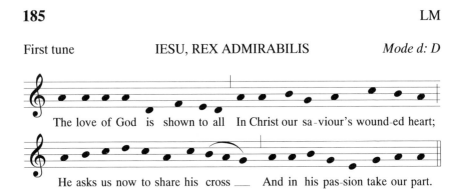

The love of God is shown to all   In Christ our sa-viour's wound-ed heart;

He asks us now to share his cross ___ And in his pas-sion take our part.

Second tune   EISENACH

THE SACRED HEART OF JESUS

1. The love of God is shown to all
    In Christ our saviour's wounded heart;
    He asks us now to share his cross
    And in his passion take our part.

2. We are the Father's gift to Christ
    Who loved his own until the end;
    His burden light we bear with joy,
    And gladly to his yoke we bend.

3. Where love and loving-kindness are,
    The God of love will always be:
    With cords of love he binds us fast,
    Yet leaves the willing captive free.

4. Praise Father, Son and Spirit blest,
    Eternal Trinity sublime,
    Who make their home in humble hearts,
    Indwelling to the end of time.

Text: Stanbrook Abbey. Second tune: melody adapted from J. H. Schein (1586-1630); harmony, editors.

Text: © 1974, Stanbrook Abbey, Callow End, Worcester WR2 4TD. Second tune (harmony): © 1995, Panel of Monastic Musicians, Mount Saint Bernard Abbey, Coalville, Leicester LE67 5UL.

186

First tune   SYNESIUS   *Mode 3: E*

To Christ, _ the prince of peace, And Son of God most high,

The Fa - ther of the world to come, Sing we with ho - ly joy.

Second tune   NARENZA

THE SACRED HEART OF JESUS

1   To Christ, the prince of peace,
    And Son of God most high,
    The Father of the world to come,
    Sing we with holy joy.

2   Deep in his heart for us
    The wound of love he bore;
    That love wherewith he still inflames
    The hearts that him adore.

3   O Jesu, victim blest,
    What else but love divine
    Could thee constrain to open thus
    That sacred heart of thine?

4   O fount of endless life,
    O spring of water clear,
    O flame celestial, cleansing all
    Who unto thee draw near,

5   Hide us in thy dear heart,
    For thither do we fly;
    There seek thy grace through life, in death
    Thine immortality.

6   Praise to the Father be,
    And sole-begotten Son;
    Praise, holy Paraclete, to thee
    While endless ages run.

Text: Edward Caswall (1814-78); from *Summi parentis Filio* (*Catholicarum Hymnologium Germanicum*, 1584). First tune: Peter Allan CR. Second tune: melody adapted from Leisentritt, *Catholicarum Hymnologium Germanicum*, Bautzen 1584; harmony, William H. Havergal (1793-1870).

First tune: © 1995, Community of the Resurrection, Mirfield, West Yorkshire WF14 0BN.

187

10.10.10.4

First tune

LAUS CHRISTI

Mode 1: D

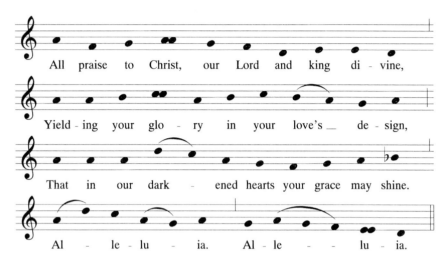

All praise to Christ, our Lord and king di - vine,

Yield - ing your glo - ry in your love's _ de - sign,

That in our dark - ened hearts your grace may shine.

Al - le - lu - ia. Al - le - - lu - ia.

1   All praise to Christ, our Lord and king divine,
        Yielding your glory in your love's design,
        That in our darkened hearts your grace may shine.
        Alleluia.

2   You came to us in lowliness of thought;
        By you the outcast and the poor were sought;
        And by your death was our redemption bought.
        Alleluia.

3   The mind of Christ is as our minds should be:
        He was a servant that we might be free,
        Humbling himself to death on Calvary.
        Alleluia.

4   And so we see in God's great purpose, how
        Christ has been raised above all creatures now;
        And at his name shall every nation bow.
        Alleluia.

5   Let every tongue confess with one accord,
        In heaven and earth, that Jesus Christ is Lord,
        And God the Father be by all adored.
        Alleluia.

CHRIST THE KING

EVENING PRAYER
Second tune   CHRISTUS REGNANS

Al - le - lu - ia.

Text: Francis Bland Tucker (1895-1984), altered; from Philippians 2 (5-11). First tune: Alan Rees OSB.
Second tune: Alan Rees OSB and John Harper.

Text: © Church Pension Fund, 445 Fifth Avenue, New York, NY 10016. First tune: © 1995, Belmont
Abbey Trustees, Hereford, HR2 9RZ. Second tune: © 1995, Panel of Monastic Musicians, Mount Saint
Bernard Abbey, Coalville, Leicester LE67 5UL.

188 LM

First tune IESU, REX ADMIRABILIS *Mode d: D*

O Je-sus, migh-ty prince of peace, Take war from each re-bel-lious heart;

U-nite with-in one com-mon fold ___ All those whom sin still keeps a-part.

1   O Jesus, mighty prince of peace,
     Take war from each rebellious heart;
     Unite within one common fold
     All those whom sin still keeps apart.

2   It was for this you opened wide
     Your arms in welcome on the tree,
     Revealing in your patient heart
     The kind of love that keeps us free.

3   We praise you mighty Lord of all,
     O Jesus, come, O Christ, O king;
     O Father, come, O Spirit, come:
     Receive the homage that we bring.

CHRIST THE KING

Second tune   BRESLAU

Text: Ralph Wright OSB; from *Te saeculorum principem*, Victor of Genoa (d. 1967). Second tune: melody, *Locheimer Gesangbuch*, 15th century, as in C. Gall, *As Hymnodus Sacer*, Leipzig 1625; harmony derived from Felix Mendelssohn (1809-47).

189

8.7.8.7

First tune   MARKYATE   *Mode d: D*

Christ is Lord, in glo-ry reign - ing, Priest for e - ver, king of _ kings,

While to him all _ glad cre-a - tion Praise and hum-ble wor-ship _ brings.

Second tune   CROSS OF JESUS

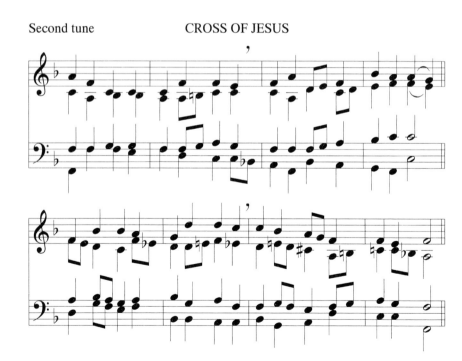

CHRIST THE KING

1   Christ is Lord, in glory reigning,
Priest for ever, king of kings,
While to him all glad creation
Praise and humble worship brings.

2   He has paid our regal ransom,
Nailed against that bitter wood:
Now the symbol of his conquest,
Royal and victorious rood.

3   When he comes again in splendour,
Cross upheld in pierced right hand,
All the power of hell shall perish
And no evil dare to stand.

4   Father, Son and Holy Spirit,
Trinity sublime we praise;
May your kingdom come among us,
Bringing peace to all our days.

Text: Stanbrook Abbey. First tune: Stanbrook Abbey. Second tune: John Stainer (1840-1901).

Text and first tune: © 1974, Stanbrook Abbey, Callow End, Worcester WR2 4TD.

Ω

THE DIURNAL

201-266

201

First tune   MEDIAE NOCTIS   *Mode 2: F♯*

A-wake, a-wake, fling off the night, For God has sent his glo-rious light;

And we who live in Christ's new day Must works of dark-ness put a-way.

Second tune   AB ASCENDENTE

OFFICE OF READINGS

1   Awake, awake, fling off the night,
     For God has sent his glorious light;
     And we who live in Christ's new day
     Must works of darkness put away.

2   Awake, arise, and be renewed,
     And with the Spirit's power endued.
     The light of life in us must glow,
     And fruits of truth and goodness show.

3   Awake, and rise up from the dead,
     And Christ his light on you will shed:
     Its power will wrong desires destroy,
     And your whole being fill with joy.

4   Then sing, rejoice, give thanks always,
     And let God's praises fill your days.
     Lift up your hearts; with one accord
     Praise God through Jesus Christ our Lord.

Text: J. R. Peacey (1896-1971), abbreviated and altered; from Ephesians 5 (6-20). Second tune: melody,
La Feillée, *Méthode du Plain-chant*, 1782; harmony, editors.

Text: © 1971, by kind permission of the Revd. M.J. Hancock, London. Second tune (harmony): ©
1995, Panel of Monastic Musicians, Mount Saint Bernard Abbey, Coalville, Leicester LE67 5UL.

202

LM

First tune   PRIMO DIERUM   *Mode 4: F♯*

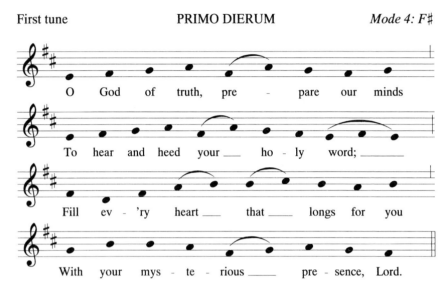

O God of truth, pre - pare our minds

To hear and heed your ___ ho - ly word; ___

Fill ev - 'ry heart ___ that ___ longs for you

With your mys - te - rious ___ pre - sence, Lord.

Second tune   NUN LASZT UNS ALL

OFFICE OF READINGS

1   O God of truth, prepare our minds
      To hear and heed your holy word;
      Fill every heart that longs for you
      With your mysterious presence, Lord.

2   The word of God for ever stands,
      Is carved upon eternal stone;
      His mouth has uttered it for us
      Who cannot live by bread alone.

3   To Father, Son and Spirit blest
      Unending praise and glory give:
      Their silent voice no ear has heard,
      Yet by their every word we live.

Text: Stanbrook Abbey, conflated. Second tune: Bohemian Brothers, *Gesangbuch*, 1544.

203

First tune · MEDIAE NOCTIS · *Mode 2: F♯*

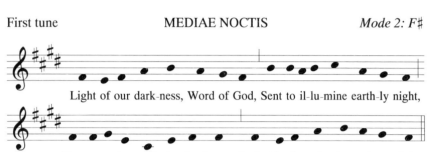

Light of our dark-ness, Word of God, Sent to il-lu-mine earth-ly night,

You we sa-lute with sing-ing hearts, Bathed in the splen-dour of your light.

Second tune · MEIN' SEEL', O GOTT

OFFICE OF READINGS

1   Light of our darkness, Word of God,
         Sent to illumine earthly night,
         You we salute with singing hearts,
         Bathed in the splendour of your light.

2   Sword that can pierce the inmost soul,
         Stripping whatever thoughts are there,
         Cut to the marrow of our minds;
         Enter our hearts and lay them bare.

3   Vessel of God's abundant life,
         Bearer of truth that sets us free,
         Breaking the deadly grasp of sin,
         Work in our hearts your mystery.

4   Word that has overcome the world,
         Seed of immortal destiny,
         Grow in our hearts, that we may live
         Sharing your deathless victory.

Text: Richard Connolly (1830-1903). Second tune: melody, Michael Praetorius (1571-1621).

204   8.7.8.7

First tune   SPONSA CHRISTI   *Mode 1: D*

God has spo-ken by his pro-phets, Spo-ken his un-chang-ing word,

Each from age to age pro-claim-ing God the one the right-eous Lord.

Second tune   REDHEAD No. 46

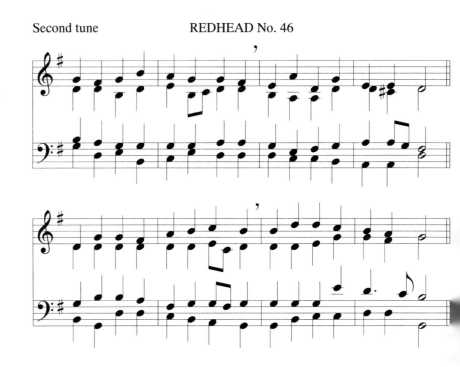

1 God has spoken by his prophets,
  Spoken his unchanging word,
  Each from age to age proclaiming
  God the one, the righteous Lord.

2 God has spoken by Christ Jesus,
  Christ, the everlasting Son,
  Brightness of the Father's glory,
  With the Father ever one.

3 God is speaking through the Spirit,
  Penetrating to the heart
  In eternal words of wisdom,
  God's own message to impart.

4 Through the rise and fall of nations
  One sure faith yet standing fast:
  God abides, his word unchanging,
  God the first and God the last.

Text: v. 1, 2, 4, G. W. Briggs (1875-1959), altered; v. 3, editors. First tune: first strain of sequence, *Sponsa Christi*, Grenoble 17th century. Second tune: Richard Redhead (1820-1901).

Text: v. 1, 2, 4, © 1953, renewal 1981 by The Hymn Society. All rights reserved. Used by permission of Hope Publishing Company, 380 South Main Place, Carol Stream, Illinois 60188; v. 3, © 1995, Panel of Monastic Musicians, Mount Saint Bernard Abbey, Coalville, Leicester LE67 5UL.

205   8.7.8.7

First tune   STONELEIGH   *Mode 2: F♯*

Who can scale the Lord's high moun-tain, Feed on pas-tures high a-bove,

Drink their fill from that clear foun-tain God's a-bound-ing stead-fast love?

Alternative: SIXLAND, 107

Second tune   SHIPSTON

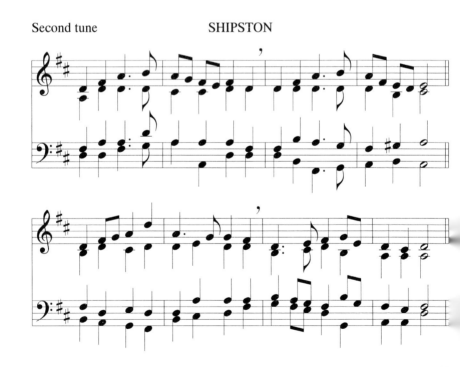

1   Who can scale the Lord's high mountain,
    Feed on pastures high above,
    Drink their fill from that clear fountain,
    God's abounding steadfast love?

2   Only those who walk in justice,
    Shape their lives by God's commands,
    And with love and self-surrender
    Satisfy the law's demands.

3   Only these whose heart is steadfast,
    Who are blameless in their ways.
    They will win the Lord's approval
    Finding blessing all their days.

4   To our God, forever faithful,
    Joyfully our voices raise.
    Glory be to God most holy,
    Blessing, power and endless praise

Text: Michael Casey OCSO. First tune: Mount Saint Bernard Abbey. Second tune: melody, Warwickshire ballad, collected Lucy Broadwood (1858-1929), arranged Ralph Vaughan Williams (1872-1958), from *The English Hymnal.*

Text © 1995, Tarrawarra Abbey, Yarra Glen, Victoria 3775, Australia. First tune: © 1995, Mount Saint Bernard Abbey, Coalville, Leicester LE67 5UL. Second tune: © Oxford University Press.

206

LM

First tune

MEDIAE NOCTIS

Mode 2: F♯

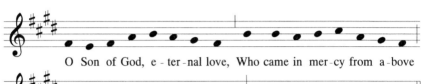

O Son of God, e - ter -nal love, Who came in mer -cy from a -bove

To bring on earth the Fa-ther's grace, And sanc-ti-fy a ran-somed race.

Second tune

DAS LEIDEN DES HERRN

1   O Son of God, eternal love,
    Who came in mercy from above
    To bring on earth the Father's grace,
    And sanctify a ransomed race.

2   Enlighten every Christian mind,
    And grant us through your Word to find
    The truth that sets the sin-bound free,
    The service that is liberty.

3   To Christ whose blood for us was shed,
    Who rose victorious from the dead,
    Whose glory all the saints adore,
    Be endless praise for evermore.

Text: G. B. Timms, altered. Second tune: melody adapted from German traditional; harmony, editors.

Text: © Oxford University Press. Second tune (harmony): © 1995, Panel of Monastic Musicians, Mount Saint Bernard Abbey, Coalville, Leicester LE67 5UL.

207

First tune   LAUDERDALE   *Mode d: F*

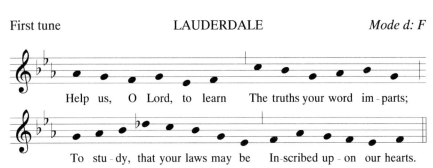

Help us, O Lord, to learn   The truths your word im-parts;

To stu-dy, that your laws may be   In-scribed up-on our hearts.

Second tune   SAINT MICHAEL

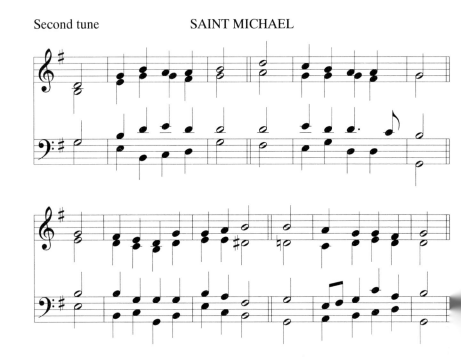

OFFICE OF READINGS

1   Help us, O Lord, to learn
     The truths your word imparts;
     To study, that your laws may be
     Inscribed upon our hearts.

2   Help us, O Lord, to live
     That faith which we proclaim,
     That all our thoughts and words and deeds
     May glorify your name.

3   Help us, O Lord, to teach
     The beauty of your ways,
     That all who seek may find the Christ,
     And make a life of praise.

Text: William Watkins Reid Junior, altered. First tune: Erik Routley (1917-82). Second tune: melody: Louis Bourgeois, Genevan Psalter, 1551, adapted by William Crotch (1775-1847).

Text: © 1959, renewal 1987 by The Hymn Society. All rights reserved. Used by permission of Hope Publishing Company, 380 South Main Place, Carol Stream, Illinois 60188. First tune: © 1982, executors of Erik Routley.

208   11.11.11.5

First tune   NOCTE SURGENTES (i)   *Mode 1: E*

Word of the Fa - ther, source of all things liv - ing;

Word_ once made flesh, _ our true and on - ly sa - viour,

Grow in our hearts,_ O seed of hea-ven's har - vest,

Je - sus, re - deem - er.

1   Word of the Father, source of all things living,
     Word once made flesh, our true and only saviour,
     Grow in our hearts, O seed of heaven's harvest,
     Jesus, redeemer.

2   Gospel from heaven, living Word incarnate,
     Open our minds, Lord, teach us your true wisdom;
     Lamp to our footsteps, scatter all our darkness,
     Day-star of glory.

3   Lord of the faithful, guide us on our journey;
     Pilgrims, we hunger for the life of heaven;
     Jesus, our manna, feed us with your goodness,
     Here and hereafter.

Second tune   CHRISTE, FONS IUGIS

Text: G. B. Timms. Second tune: melody, Philippe Dubois, Paris Antiphoner, 1681; harmony, Ralph Vaughan Williams (1872-1958), from *The English Hymnal*.

209

CM

First tune   HUDDLESTON   *Mode 2: F*

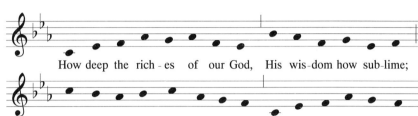

How deep the rich-es of our God, His wis-dom how sub-lime;

How high his judg-ments soar a-bove All judg-ment of man-kind.

1   How deep the riches of our God,
        His wisdom how sublime;
        How high his judgments soar above
        All judgment of mankind.

2   What mind has read the mind of God,
        Or given him counsel sure?
        Who from his riches gave to God
        What was not first received?

3   From God all things created flow;
        All things through him exist;
        To him for judgment all return,
        To whom all praise is due.

4   To God the Father, fount of grace,
        Through his beloved Son,
        With God their Spirit, bond of love,
        Be glory evermore.

Second tune   SAINT BOTOLPH

Text: James Quinn SJ; from Romans 2 (33-6). First tune: *The Anglican Office Book*. Second tune: Gordon Slater (1896-1979).

210

First tune   **VAVASOUR**   *Mode 3: E*

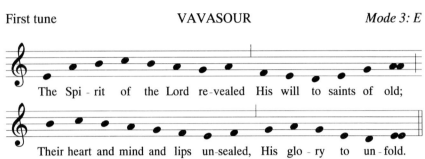

The Spi - rit of the Lord re-vealed His will to saints of old;

Their heart and mind and lips un-sealed, His glo - ry to un - fold.

Second tune   **SAINT JAMES**

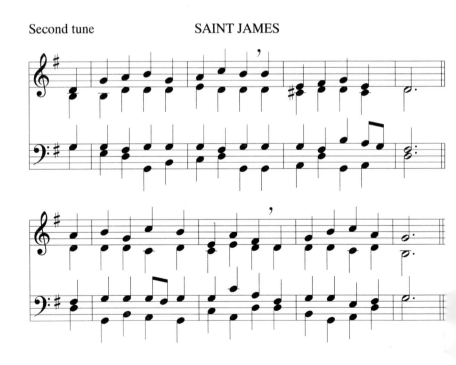

1   The Spirit of the Lord revealed
     His will to saints of old;
     Their heart and mind and lips unsealed,
     His glory to unfold.

2   Eternal Spirit, you that speak
     To mind and conscience still,
     That we, in this our day, may seek
     To do our Father's will;

3   To us the word of life impart,
     Of Christ, the living way;
     Give us a quiet, humble heart
     To listen and obey.

Text: G. W. Briggs (1875-1959), abbreviated and altered. First tune: Stanbrook Abbey. Second tune: R. Courtville, 1697.

Text: © Oxford University Press. First tune: © 1974, Stanbrook Abbey, Callow End, Worcester WR2 3TD.

211

8.7.8.7

First tune   SPONSA CHRISTI   Mode 1: D

Wor-ship, glo - ry, praise and ho -nour   To   our God, high-throned a -bove;

We with ma - ny   ge - ne - ra-tions, Join   to praise your name of love.

Second tune   REDHEAD No. 46

1   Worship, glory, praise and honour
     To our God, high-throned above:
     We, with many generations,
     Join to praise your name of love.

2   In the scriptures, by the Spirit,
     May we see the saviour's face,
     Hear his word and heed his calling,
     Know his will and grow in grace.

3   Praise the everlasting Father
     And the Word, his only Son;
     Praise them through the Holy Spirit,
     Perfect Trinity in One.

Text: Bishop Maurice Wood, abbreviated and altered. First tune: first strain of sequence, *Sponsa Christi,* Grenoble 17th century. Second tune: Richard Redhead (1820-1901).

212   7.8.7.8.8.8

First tune   IUDICA ME   *Mode 1: D*

Word of God, come down on earth, Liv-ing rain from heav'n de-scend-ing;

Touch our hearts and bring to __ birth Faith and hope and love un-end - ing.

Word al-migh-ty, we re-vere you; Word made flesh, we long to hear you.

1   Word of God, come down on earth,
     Living rain from heaven descending;
     Touch our hearts and bring to birth
     Faith and hope and love unending.
     Word almighty, we revere you;
     Word made flesh, we long to hear you.

2   Word eternal, throned on high,
     Word that brought to life creation,
     Word that came from heaven to die,
     Crucified for our salvation,
     Saving Word, the world restoring,
     Speak to us, your love outpouring.

3   Word that speaks your Father's love,
     One with him beyond all telling,
     Word that sends us from above
     God the Spirit, with us dwelling,
     Word of truth, to all truth lead us,
     Word of life, with one Bread feed us.

Second tune   LIEBSTER JESU

Text: James Quinn SJ, abbreviated. First tune: Cecilia Cavenaugh OC. Second tune: melody adapted from Johann Rudolph Ahle (1625-73).

Text: © 1969, James Quinn SJ and Geoffrey Chapman, a Cassell imprint, Wellington House, Strand, London WC2R 0BB. First tune: © 1995, Saint Bernard's Convent, Slough, Berkshire SL3 7AF.

213　　　　　　　　　　　　　　　　　　　　　　　7.6.7.6

First tune　　　　　　　　　**WHALLEY**　　　　　　　　*Mode 1: D*

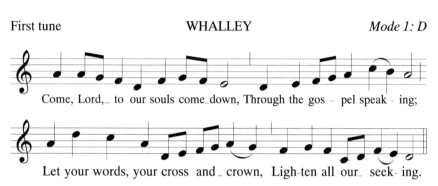

Come, Lord,_ to our souls come_down, Through the gos - pel speak - ing;

Let your words, your cross and _ crown, Ligh-ten all our_ seek- ing.

Second tune　　　　　　　　　**CULBACH**

1   Come, Lord, to our souls come down,
    Through the gospel speaking;
    Let your words, your cross and crown,
    Lighten all our seeking.

2   Drive out darkness from the heart,
    Banish pride and blindness;
    Plant in every inward part
    Truthfulness and kindness.

3   Eyes be open, spirits stirred,
    Minds new truth receiving;
    Stir us, Lord, by your own word;
    Deepen our believing.

Text: H. C. A. Gaunt (1902-83), altered. First tune: Mount Saint Bernard Abbey. Second tune: adapted from Scheffler, *Heilige Seelenlust*, 1657.

Text: © Oxford University Press. First tune: © 1995, Mount Saint Bernard Abbey, Coalville, Leicester LE67 5UL.

214

6.5.6.5

First tune   **LLANIESTYN**   *Mode 1: F*

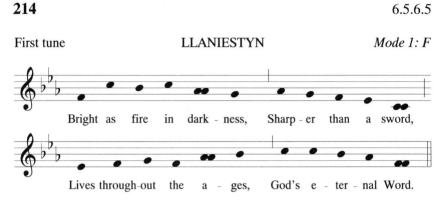

Bright as fire in darkness, Sharp-er than a sword,

Lives through-out the a - ges, God's e - ter - nal Word.

Second tune   **WESTHEAD**

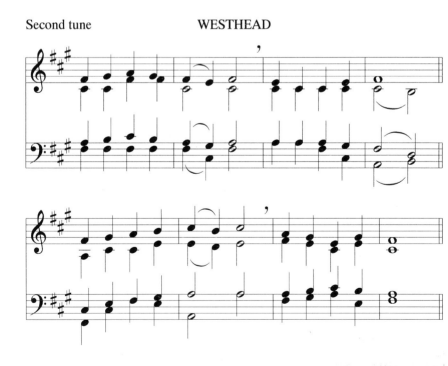

OFFICE OF READINGS

1   Bright as fire in darkness,
Sharper than a sword,
Lives throughout the ages,
God's eternal Word.

2   Christ, your eyes of mercy
See our sins revealed;
Speak the word that saves us,
That we may be healed.

3   Father, Son and Spirit,
Trinity of might,
Compassed in your glory,
Give the world your light.

Text: Stanbrook Abbey, conflated. First tune: John Harper. Second tune: melody, Stanbrook Abbey; harmony, John Harper.

Text and second tune (melody): © 1974, Stanbrook Abbey, Callow End, Worcester WR2 4TD. First tune and second tune (harmony): © 1995, Panel of Monastic Musicians, Mount Saint Bernard Abbey, Coalville, Leicester LE67 5UL.

215

First tune   PRIMO DIERUM   *Mode 4: F♯*

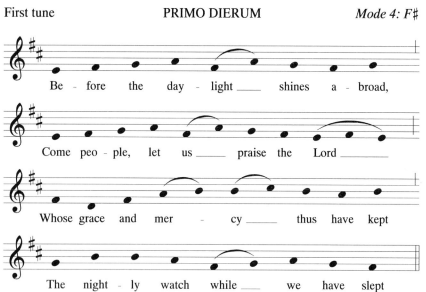

Be - fore the day - light ___ shines a - broad,

Come peo - ple, let us ___ praise the Lord ___

Whose grace and mer - cy ___ thus have kept

The night - ly watch while ___ we have slept

1   Before the daylight shines abroad,
        Come people, let us praise the Lord
        Whose grace and mercy thus have kept
        The nightly watch while we have slept.

2   In heart and voice and spirit one,
        The Lord's new song is now begun;
        We sing of mercies ever new
        And faithful love, so strong and true.

3   God's love has called us from our sleep
        To ponder mysteries so deep,
        To praise the glory of his grace
        Revealed to us on Christ's own face.

4   We offer up ourselves to you
        In all we think or say or do,
        Our glory now and evermore,
        Our joy, our God, whom we adore

Second tune   GOTT SCHUF ADAM

Text: attribution unknown, altered. Second tune: N. Herman, 1563.

216

CM

First tune   HUDDLESTON   *Mode 2: F*

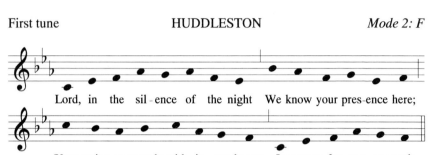

Lord, in the sil-ence of the night We know your pres-ence here;

Your voice re-sounds with-in our hearts, In prayer, for you we wait.

Second tune   CAITHNESS

VIGILS

1   Lord, in the silence of the night
     We know your presence here;
     Your voice resounds within our hearts,
     In prayer, for you we wait.

2   Great Word of God, in darkest night
     You came, like falling dew.
     O Saviour, light of all the world,
     Be with us at this hour.

3   Lord, in the stillness of the night
     Your Spirit moves and breathes;
     Strength of all being and all life,
     Enfold us in your love.

Text: editors; inspired by a text from West Malling Abbey. First tune: *The Anglican Office Book*. Second tune: melody from the Scottish Psalter, 1635.

Text: © 1995, Panel of Monastic Musicians, Mount Saint Bernard Abbey, Coalville, Leicester LE67 5UL. First tune: © 1981, Communities Consultative Council (Anglican Religious Communities), PO Box 17, Eccleshall, Stafford ST21 6LB.

217

10.7.10.6

FURNESS

Mode 2: F♯

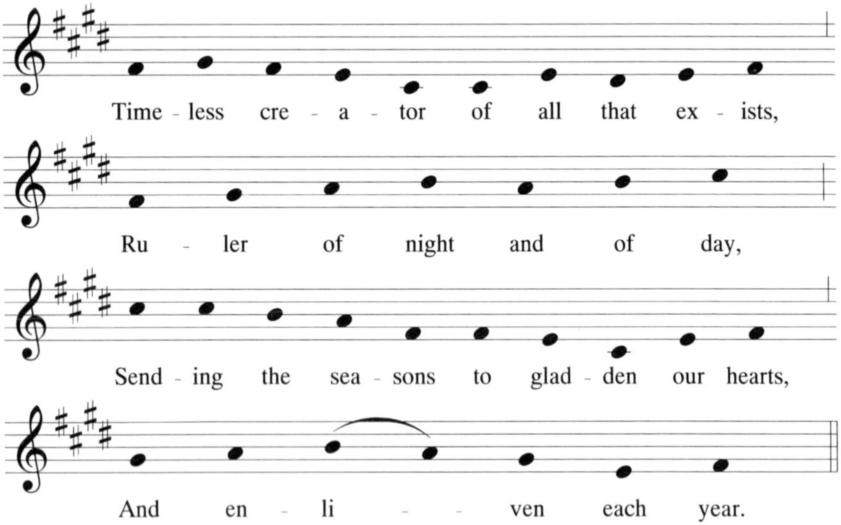

Time - less cre - a - tor of all that ex - ists,

Ru - ler of night and of day,

Send - ing the sea - sons to glad - den our hearts,

And en - li - ven each year.

217

1   Timeless creator of all that exists,
     Ruler of night and of day,
     Sending the seasons to gladden our hearts,
     And enliven each year.

2   Look on us, Jesus, we falter and fail:
     Strengthen and heal by your gaze;
     Turn but towards us and guilt falls away,
     Washed by life-giving tears.

3   You are the sun that must shine on our hearts,
     Scattering sleep from our minds;
     Now before dawn let our voices be raised
     In the praise that we owe.

4   Let us give glory to God, as is due,
     Glory to Jesus, his Son,
     Glory to him who is Spirit of both,
     Through all ages to come.

Text: Mount Saint Bernard Abbey; from *Aeterne rerum conditor*, Saint Ambrose (c. 339-397). Tune: Mount Saint Bernard Abbey.

Text and tune: © 1995, Mount Saint Bernard Abbey, Coalville, Leicester LE67 5UL.

218   11.11.11.5

First tune   NOCTE SURGENTES (ii)   *Mode 6: A*

Fa - ther of ___ mer - cies, heaven's e - ter - nal day - spring,

Ma - ker of all things, shine on your cre - a - tion;

Vi - sit your child - ren, born to share your glo - ry,

Heirs of your king - dom.

1   Father of mercies, heaven's eternal dayspring,
     Maker of all things, shine on your creation;
     Visit your children, born to share your glory,
     Heirs of your kingdom.

2   Son of the Father, splendour born of splendour,
     Star of the morning, sun that knows no setting,
     Come now in blessing, God's true Word and Wisdom,
     Dawn of salvation.

3   Spirit of Jesus, fire of love descending,
     Warmth of our spirit, light when all is darkness,
     Strength in our weakness, joy in every sorrow,
     Be with us always.

Second tune　　　　　　　CHRISTE, FONS IUGIS

Text: James Quinn SJ. Second tune: melody, Philippe Dubois, Paris Antiphoner, 1681; harmony, Ralph Vaughan Williams (1872-1958), from *The English Hymnal*.

219 LM

First tune **MEDIAE NOCTIS** *Mode 2: F♯*

With minds re-freshed by rest a-gain, We rise to praise your ho-ly name:

Be near us, Fa-ther, as we sing; Ac-cept our morn-ing of - fer-ing.

Second tune **ROUEN**

VIGILS

1   With minds refreshed by rest again,
    We rise to praise your holy name:
    Be near us, Father, as we sing;
    Accept our morning offering.

2   To you our voices raise their song;
    For you our fervent spirits long;
    In you, we pray, O holy one,
    Be all our acts this day begun.

3   As now the dark to light gives way,
    And night gives place to dawn of day:
    So may the evils of the night
    Be shattered by the gift of light.

4   O hear us, Father, as we pray
    That all our faults be put away;
    And may the tongues that sing your praise
    Give thanks to you through endless days.

5   Most holy Father, grant our prayer,
    And Christ, who does his glory share;
    With both, the Spirit we adore,
    One only God for evermore.

Text: Farnborough Abbey, altered. Second tune: melody, Rouen Antiphoner, 1728; harmony, Stephen Dean.

Second tune (harmony): © 1972, Stephen Dean, Oregon Catholic Press, 5536 N.E. Hassalo, Portland, Oregon 97213.

220

11.11.11.5

First tune ECCE IAM NOCTIS *Mode 4: G*

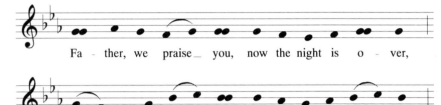

Fa - ther, we praise — you, now the night is o - ver,

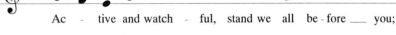

Ac - tive and watch - ful, stand we all be - fore __ you;

Sing - ing, we of - fer __ pray'r and a - do - ra - tion:

Thus we ad - ore __ you.

1 Father, we praise you, now the night is over,
  Active and watchful, stand we all before you;
  Singing, we offer prayer and adoration:
  Thus we adore you.

2 Monarch of all things, fit us for your kingdom;
  Banish our weakness, health and wholeness sending;
  Bring us to heaven, where your saints united
  Joy without ending.

3 All-holy Father, Son and equal Spirit,
  Trinity blessed, send us your salvation;
  Yours is the glory, filling all creation,
  Ever resounding.

Second tune   AD TUUM NOMEN

Text: Percy Dearmer (1867-1936), altered; from *Nocte surgentes* (8th or 9th century). Second tune: melody, Chartres Antiphoner, 1784; harmony, John Harper.

Text: © Oxford University Press. Second tune (harmony): © 1995, Panel of Monastic Musicians, Mount Saint Bernard Abbey, Coalville, Leicester LE67 5UL.

221

First tune · SPLENDOR PATERNAE GLORIAE · *Mode 1:D*

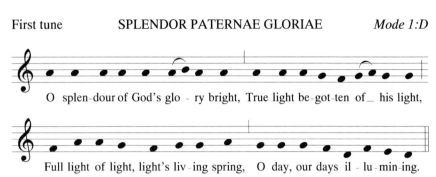

O splen-dour of God's glo - ry bright, True light be-got-ten of _ his light,

Full light of light, light's liv-ing spring, O day, our days il - lu-min-ing.

Second tune · DIE GANZE WELT (HILARITER)

MORNING PRAYER

1 O splendour of God's glory bright,
  True light begotten of his light,
  Full light of light, light's living spring,
  O day, our days illumining,

2 Come, righteous sun of heavenly love,
  Pour down your radiance from above;
  And shed the Holy Spirit's ray
  On every thought and sense today.

3 With prayer the Father we implore,
  The Father glorious evermore:
  Almighty, source of grace and power,
  Be with us in temptation's hour,

4 To guide whatever we may do,
  With love all envy to subdue,
  To give us grace to bear all wrong,
  Transforming sorrow into song.

5 All laud to you, O Father be,
  To you, O Son, eternally;
  To you, the Spirit, equal praise
  From joyful hearts we ever raise.

Text: Robert Bridges (1844-1930), altered; from *Splendor paternae gloriae*, Saint Ambrose (c. 339-397). Second tune: melody, *Kölner Gesangbuch*, 1623; harmony: Redmund Shaw, altered.

Text: © Oxford University Press. Second tune: © 1971, Redmund Shaw; by permission of Paul Inwood.

222

7.6.7.6

First tune   EANSWYTHE   *Mode 2: F*

O Christ, the light of hea-ven, And of the world true light,

You come in all your ra-diance To cleave the web — of night.

Second tune   CHRISTUS, DER IST MEIN LEBEN

MORNING PRAYER

1   O Christ, the light of heaven,
     And of the world true light,
     You come in all your radiance
     To cleave the web of night.

2   May what is false within us
     Before your truth give way,
     That we may live untroubled
     With quiet hearts this day.

3   May steadfast faith sustain us
     And hope made firm in you;
     The love that we have wasted,
     O God of love, renew.

4   Blest Trinity we praise you
     In whom our quest will cease;
     Keep us with you for ever
     In happiness and peace.

Text: Stanbrook Abbey. First tune: Stanbrook Abbey. Second tune: melody, Melchior Vulpius (1560-1616); harmony, adapted from J. S. Bach (1685-1750).

Text and first tune: © 1974, Stanbrook Abbey, Callow End, Worcester WR2 4TD. Second tune (harmony, this version): © 1995, Panel of Monastic Musicians, Mount Saint Bernard Abbey, Coalville, Leicester E67 5UL.

223   11.11.11.5

First tune   ECCE IAM NOCTIS   *Mode 4: D*

See, now the sha - dows of the night are fad - ing,

Sun - light a - ris - ing, dawn of day in splend - our;

Spi - rit en-light - ened, ____ to the might-y Fa - ther

Pray we de - vout - ly.

1   See, now the shadows of the night are fading,
     Sunlight arising, dawn of day in splendour;
     Spirit enlightened, to the mighty Father
     Pray we devoutly,

2   That in his mercy he may always keep us,
     Eager and ready for his holy service;
     Then may he give us, of a father's goodness,
     Joy in his kingdom.

3   This may he grant us, God for ever blessed,
     Father eternal, Son and Holy Spirit:
     His is the glory filling all creation,
     Ever resounding.

Second tune   AD TUUM NOMEN

xt: editors' compilation; from *Ecce iam noctis*, Alcuin? (c. 735-804). Second tune: melody, Chartres
ntiphoner, 1784; harmony, John Harper.

xt and second tune (harmony): © 1995, Panel of Monastic Musicians, Mount Saint Bernard Abbey,
)alville, Leicester LE67 5UL.

224   LM

First tune   SPLENDOR PATERNAE GLORIAE   *Mode 1: G*

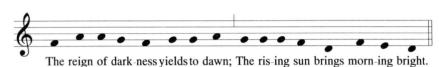

Great Lord of splen-dour, source of light, Your gen-tle rays dis-pel our night.

The reign of dark-ness yields to dawn; The ris-ing sun brings morn-ing bright.

Second tune   ZEUCH MEINER GEIST (SAINT GREGORY)

MORNING PRAYER

1   Great Lord of splendour, source of light,
Your gentle rays dispel our night.
The reign of darkness yields to dawn;
The rising sun brings morning bright.

2   Lord Jesus, day-star from on high,
Your rising welcomes in our dawn,
True morning star which never sets,
Enlightening all who are forlorn.

3   More radiant than the noonday sun,
Life-giving grace to every soul,
Shine in the darkness of our hearts;
Complete your healing, make us whole.

4   Yours is a realm of truth and life,
Of justice, peace and righteousness:
Your praise we sing, O Trinity,
Forever God in holiness.

ext: Gethsemani Abbey, altered; from *Lucis largitor splendide* (before 6th century). Second tune:
önig, *Choralbuch*, 1738.

ext: © 1975, Gethsemani Abbey, 3642 Monks Road, Trappist, Kentucky 40051.

225 LM

First tune   **AETERNE RERUM CONDITOR**   *Mode 1: D*

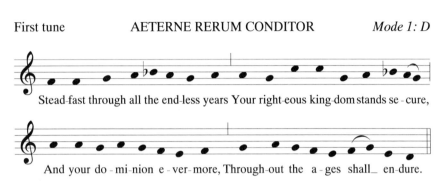

Stead-fast through all the end-less years Your right-eous king-dom stands se - cure,

And your do - mi -nion e - ver-more, Through-out the a - ges shall__ en-dure.

Second tune   **DAS NEUGEBORNE KINDELEIN (JENA)**

MORNING PRAYER

1   Steadfast through all the endless years
     Your righteous kingdom stands secure,
     And your dominion evermore,
     Throughout the ages shall endure.

2   O Lord, you by the Father's will
     Came as incarnate Son to earth,
     And stooped so humbly from your throne
     To share with us a lowly birth.

3   O Lord, you came on us to shine,
     True light from the eternal light;
     And now the Father's brightness rests
     On those who long have dwelt in night.

4   O see how everything that breathes
     Its homage gives, in deed and word,
     The glory of almighty God,
     The Father's image, Christ our Lord.

5   We bless you, Father, fount of light,
     And Christ, your well-beloved Son,
     Who with the Spirit dwell in us:
     Immortal Trinity in One.

Text: James Brownlie (1857-1925), altered; from the Greek, Anatolius (9th century). Second tune: melody, Melchior Vulpius (c. 1560-1616); harmony, adapted from J. S. Bach (1685-1750).

Text (this version): © 1995, Panel of Monastic Musicians, Mount Saint Bernard Abbey, Coalville, Leicester LE67 5UL.

226 LM

First tune   LUCIS LARGITOR SPLENDIDE   *Mode 4: G*

E-ter-nal glo-ry _ fills the heav'n, Our on-ly hope in _ mer-cy giv'n:

Christ Je-sus, whom a _ vir-gin bore, Son of the Fa-ther_ e-ver-more.

1   Eternal glory fills the heaven,
      Our only hope, in mercy given:
      Christ Jesus, whom a virgin bore,
      Son of the Father evermore.

2   The morning star shines bright and clear
      Announcing that the day is near.
      Lord, grant us strength our hearts to raise,
      That we this day may sing your praise.

3   Night's shadows fade: Lord, on us shine;
      Our darkness turn to light divine;
      Then in that light our life may rest,
      Renewed by grace, and by you blest.

4   Let faith assume the foremost part,
      Be firmly rooted in the heart;
      And joyous hope in second place,
      Then love may reign, your greatest grace.

5   All glory to the Father be,
      And to the Son, eternally;
      And to the Spirit, equal praise
      From joyful hearts we ever raise.

Text: editors' compilation; from *Aeterna caeli gloria* (7th or 8th century). Second tune: William Knapp (1698-1768).

Text: © 1995, Panel of Monastic Musicians, Mount Saint Bernard Abbey, Coalville, Leicester LE67 5UL.

Second tune   WAREHAM

227

LM

First tune   AETERNE RERUM CONDITOR   *Mode 1: D*

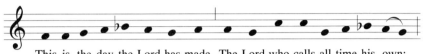

This is the day the Lord has made, The Lord who calls all time his own; _

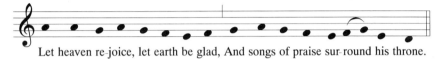

Let heaven re-joice, let earth be glad, And songs of praise sur-round his throne.

Second tune   O AMOR QUAM EXSTATICUS (RESURREXIT)

MORNING PRAYER

1   This is the day the Lord has made,
    The Lord who calls all time his own;
    Let heaven rejoice, let earth be glad,
    And songs of praise surround his throne.

2   Blest be the Lord who came to us,
    Bestowing heavenly truth and grace;
    Who came in God the Father's name
    To save this sinful human race.

3   This is the day he rose from death,
    And Satan's futile empire fell;
    Now through the world his triumph spread
    And all his mighty wonders tell.

4   To God the Father, glory be,
    And to his well-beloved Son,
    Who with the Spirit dwell in us:
    Immortal Trinity in One.

Text: Isaac Watts (1674-1748), altered. Second tune: French church melody; harmony, Ralph Vaughan Williams (1872-1958), from *The English Hymnal*, altered.

Text (this version): © 1995, Panel of Monastic Musicians, Mount Saint Bernard Abbey, Coalville, Leicester LE67 5UL. Second tune (harmony): © Oxford University Press. Altered by permission.

228

First tune SPLENDOR PATERNAE GLORIAE *Mode 1: G*

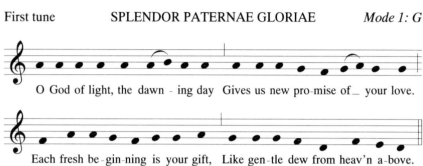

O God of light, the dawn - ing day Gives us new pro-mise of _ your love.

Each fresh be -gin-ning is your gift, Like gen-tle dew from heav'n a-bove.

Second tune MELCOMBE

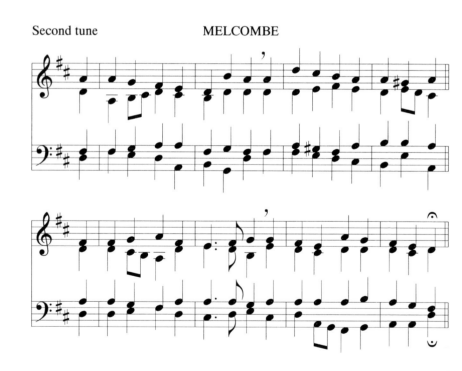

MORNING PRAYER

1   O God of light, the dawning day
        Gives us new promise of your love.
        Each fresh beginning is your gift,
        Like gentle dew from heaven above.

2   Your blessings, Father, never fail:
        Your Son, who is our daily bread,
        The Holy Spirit of your love,
        By whom each day your Church is led.

3   Make us the servants of your peace,
        Renew our strength, remove all fear;
        Be with us, Lord, throughout this day,
        For all is joy if you are near.

4   To Father, Son and Spirit blest,
        One only God, we humbly pray;
        Show us the splendour of your light
        In death, the dawn of perfect day.

Text: James Quinn SJ. Second tune: Samuel Webbe (1740-1816).

Text: © 1969, James Quinn SJ and Geoffrey Chapman, a Cassell imprint, Wellington House, Strand, London WC2R 0BB.

229 LM

First tune   **LUCIS LARGITOR SPLENDIDE**   *Mode 4: G*

The beau-ty of the _ ris-ing sun, Be-gins to flood the _ world with light;

A-wa-kened, na-ture glows with life As form and co-lour _ re-ap-pear.

Second tune   **ADESTO SANCTA TRINITAS**

MORNING PRAYER

1   The beauty of the rising sun,
     Begins to flood the world with light;
     Awakened, nature glows with life
     As form and colour reappear.

2   Lord Jesus Christ, since time began
     The morning sun you far outshone;
     We turn to you with joyous praise
     To ask the blessing of your grace.

3   You are God's knowledge infinite,
     His Word, through whom all things were made;
     These wonders fill our hearts with awe,
     And draw our minds to you in prayer.

4   Give us your light, that we may learn
     To walk with care the path of life;
     May all our ways and actions show
     The gifts which God on us bestows.

5   Most loving Father, hear our prayer
     Through Jesus Christ, your only Son;
     Both with the Holy Spirit reign
     For ever One and ever Three.

Text: *The Anglican Office Book*, altered. Second tune: melody, Chartres Antiphoner, 1784; harmony, Ralph Vaughan Williams (1872-1958), from *The English Hymnal*, altered.

Text: © 1981, Communities Consultative Council (Anglican Religious Communities), PO Box 17, Eccleshall, Stafford ST21 6LB. Second tune (harmony): © Oxford University Press. Altered by permission.

230   11.11.11.5

First tune   ECCE IAM NOCTIS   *Mode 4: G*

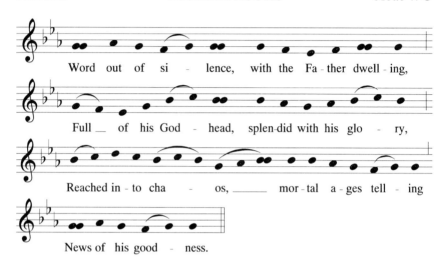

Word out of si - lence, with the Fa - ther dwell - ing,

Full __ of his God - head, splen-did with his glo - ry,

Reached in - to cha - os, _____ mor - tal a - ges tell - ing

News of his good - ness.

1   Word out of silence, with the Father dwelling,
        Full of his Godhead, splendid with his glory,
        Reached into chaos, mortal ages telling
        News of his goodness.

2   Taking our nature, to the world proclaiming
        Time for repentance, summoned his disciples;
        Healing all illness, scorn and hatred bearing,
        Feasted with sinners.

3   Dying he conquered, prince of life victorious,
        Bringing release to spirits long-imprisoned;
        Rising to heaven, now he reigns all-glorious,
        One with the Father.

4   Christ our redeemer, bearer of salvation,
        Humbly your people render thanks and glory:
        Called forth from darkness, we your priestly nation,
        Sing forth your praises.

Second tune AD TUUM NOMEN

Text: Michael Casey OCSO, altered. Second tune: melody, Chartres Antiphoner, 1784; harmony, John Harper.

Text: © Tarrawarra Abbey, Yarra Glen, Victoria 3775, Australia. Second tune (harmony): © 1995, Panel of Monastic Musicians, Mount Saint Bernard Abbey, Coalville, Leicester LE67 5UL.

231   7.6.7.6

First tune   SAWLEY   *Mode 8: F*

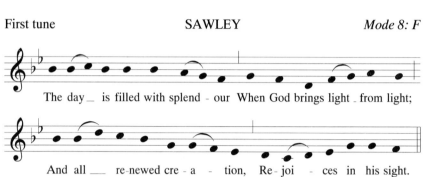

The day _ is filled with splend - our When God brings light _ from light;
And all ___ re-newed cre - a - tion, Re - joi - ces in his sight.

Second tune   CHRISTUS, DER IST MEIN LEBEN

MORNING PRAYER

1   The day is filled with splendour
    When God brings light from light;
    And all renewed creation,
    Rejoices in his sight.

2   The Father gives his children
    The wonder of the world
    In which his power and glory
    Like banners are unfurled.

3   With every living creature,
    Awaking with the day,
    We turn to God our Father,
    Lift up our hearts and pray:

4   O Father, Son and Spirit,
    Your grace and mercy send,
    That we may live to praise you
    Today and to the end.

Text: Stanbrook Abbey. First tune: Mount Saint Bernard Abbey. Second tune: melody, Melchior Vulpius (1560-1616); harmony, editors, adapted from J. S. Bach (1685-1750).

Text: © 1974, Stanbrook Abbey, Callow End, Worcester WR2 4TD. First tune: © 1995, Mount Saint Bernard Abbey, Coalville, Leicester LE67 5UL. Second tune (harmony): © 1995, Panel of Monastic Musicians, Mount Saint Bernard Abbey, Coalville, Leicester LE67 5UL.

232   LM

First tune   **AETERNE RERUM CONDITOR**   *Mode 1: D*

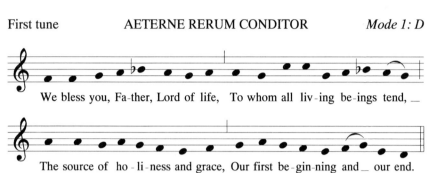

We bless you, Fa-ther, Lord of life, To whom all liv-ing be-ings tend, —

The source of ho-li-ness and grace, Our first be-gin-ning and — our end.

Second tune   **SONG 34**

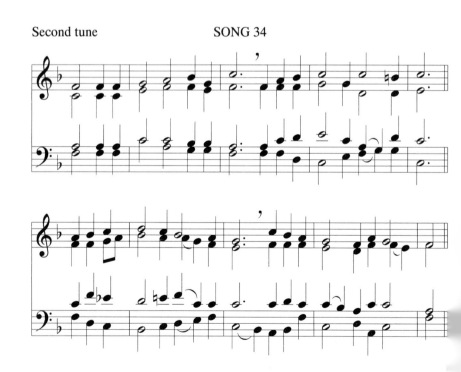

MORNING PRAYER

1   We bless you, Father, Lord of life,
    To whom all living beings tend,
    The source of holiness and grace,
    Our first beginning and our end.

2   We give you thanks, redeeming Christ,
    Who bore our weight of sin and shame:
    In dark defeat, you conquered sin,
    And death, by dying, overcame.

3   Come, Holy Spirit, searching fire,
    Whose flame all evil burns away;
    With light and love come down to us,
    In silence and in peace to stay.

4   We praise you, Trinity in One,
    Sublime in majesty and might,
    Who reign for ever, Lord of all,
    In splendour and unending light.

Text: Stanbrook Abbey. Second tune: melody and bass, Orlando Gibbons (1583-1625).

Text: © 1974, Stanbrook Abbey, Callow End, Worcester WR2 4TD.

233

LM

First tune   LUCIS LARGITOR SPLENDIDE   *Mode 4: G*

The Fa - ther's glo - ry, _____ Christ our light,

With love and mer - cy _____ comes to bless

Our fall - en world, and _____ be the way

That leads from sin to _____ ho - li - ness.

1   The Father's glory, Christ our light,
       With love and mercy comes to bless
       Our fallen world, and be the way
       That leads from sin to holiness.

2   Christ yesterday and Christ today,
       For all eternity the same,
       The image of our hidden God:
       Eternal wisdom is his name.

3   He keeps his word from age to age,
       Is with us to the end of days:
       A cloud by day, a flame by night,
       To go before us on his ways.

4   We bless you Father, fount of light,
       And Christ, your well-beloved Son,
       Who with the Spirit dwell in us:
       Immortal Trinity in One.

MORNING PRAYER

Second tune   CAELESTIS AGNI

Text: Stanbrook Abbey. Second tune: melody, Grenoble Antiphoner, 1753; harmony, John Harper.

Text: © 1974 and 1995, Stanbrook Abbey, Callow End, Worcester WR2 4TD. Second tune (harmony): © 1995, Panel of Monastic Musicians, Mount Saint Bernard Abbey, Coalville, Leicester LU67 5UL.

234

First tune   LITTLE HOURS (SUNDAY)   *Mode 2: E*

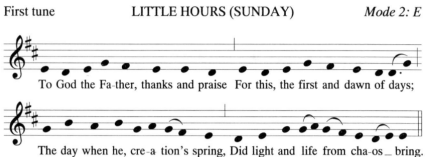

To God the Fa-ther, thanks and praise For this, the first and dawn of days;

The day when he, cre-a tion's spring, Did light and life from cha-os _ bring.

Alternatives: LITTLE HOURS, 237

Second tune   SO TREIBEN WIR

MIDDAY PRAYER

1 To God the Father, thanks and praise
For this, the first and dawn of days;
The day when he, creation's spring,
Did light and life from chaos bring.

2 The day on which his well-loved Son
O'er death and hell the triumph won;
The day on which their Spirit came,
Their gift to all, in wind and flame.

3 To God our Father, through his Son,
And in the Spirit, with them one,
We, new-created on this day,
New songs of love and glory pay.

Text: Blackfriars, Oxford, altered. Second tune: melody, Wittenberg, 1541; harmony, G. R. Woodward (1848-1934).

Text: © 1995, Order of Preachers, Blackfriars, Oxford OX1 3LY.

235

8.8.8

First tune   **NUNKEELING**   *Mode 8: D*

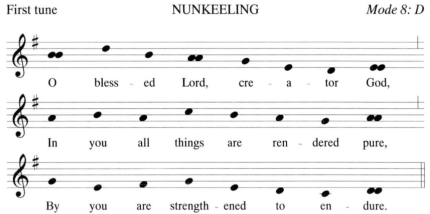

O bless - ed Lord, cre - a - tor God,

In you all things are ren - dered pure,

By you are strength - ened to en - dure.

Second tune   **O MENSCH, SIEH (BOHEMIA)**

MIDDAY PRAYER

1   O blessed Lord, creator God,
In you all things are rendered pure,
By you are strengthened to endure.

2   O blessed, holy hand of God,
All things are sanctified by you;
Adorned, enriched, you make them new.

3   O blessed majesty of God,
Containing all that you have filled;
All things are done as you have willed.

4   O blessed, holy Trinity,
Serene and certain in your ways;
You are the light of endless days.

Text and first tune: Stanbrook Abbey. Second tune: melody adapted from Bohemian Brethren, Gesangbuch, 1566.

Text and first tune: © 1974, Stanbrook Abbey, Callow End, Worcester WR2 4TD.

236

CM

First tune   EWENNY   *Mode 1: F♯*

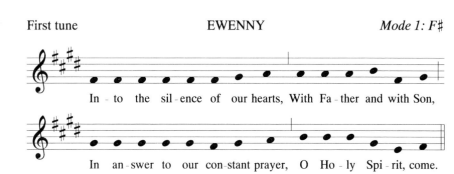

In - to the sil - ence of our hearts, With Fa - ther and with Son,

In an - swer to our con - stant prayer, O Ho - ly Spi - rit, come.

Second tune   SAINT FLAVIAN

MIDDAY PRAYER (TERCE)

1   Into the silence of our hearts,
            With Father and with Son,
            In answer to our constant prayer,
            O Holy Spirit, come.

2   Then every thought and word of ours
            With wonder will inspire,
            And all will find in us that love
            Which you alone may fire.

3   Most holy Father, grant our prayer
            Through Christ your only Son,
            That in your Spirit we may live
            And praise you ever One.

Text: Ralph Wright OSB; from *Nunc sancte nobis Spiritus*, Saint Ambrose? (c. 339-397). First tune: Laurence Bévenot OSB (1901-90). Second tune: adapted from John Day, *The Whole Psalmes*, c.1563, by Richard Redhead for Metzler, *Ancient Hymn Melodies*, 1859.

237   LM

First tunes   **LITTLE HOURS**

A: On ordinary days   *Mode d: G*

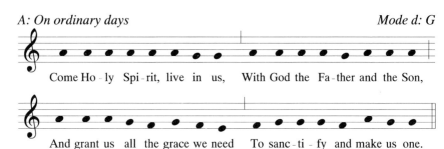

Come Ho‑ly Spi‑rit, live in us, With God the Fa‑ther and the Son,

And grant us all the grace we need To sanc‑ti‑fy and make us one.

B: On lesser feast days   *Mode 8: F*

Come Ho‑ly Spi rit, live in us, __ With God the Fa ‑ ther and the Son, __

And grant us all the grace we need __ To sanc‑ti‑fy and make us one.

C: On feast days   *Mode 8: G*

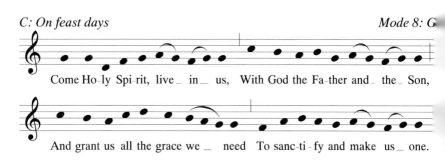

Come Ho‑ly Spi‑rit, live _ in _ us, With God the Fa‑ther and _ the _ Son,

And grant us all the grace we _ need To sanc‑ti‑fy and make us _ one.

Text: Stanbrook Abbey; from *Nunc sancte nobis Spiritus*, Saint Ambrose? (c. 339‑397). Second tune:
Peter Hurford.

Text: © 1974 and 1995, Stanbrook Abbey, Callow End, Worcester WR2 4TD. Second tune: © Oxford
University Press, Oxford OX2 6DP.

Second tune

THE HOLY SON

1   Come, Holy Spirit, live in us,
     With God the Father and the Son,
     And grant us all the grace we need
     To sanctify and make us one.

2   May mind and tongue, made strong in love,
     Your praise throughout the world proclaim;
     And may that love within our hearts
     Set fire to others with its flame.

3   Most blessed Trinity of love,
     For whom each human heart was made,
     To you be praise in timeless song,
     And everlasting homage paid.

238   LM

First tunes   **LITTLE HOURS**

A: On ordinary days   *Mode d: G*

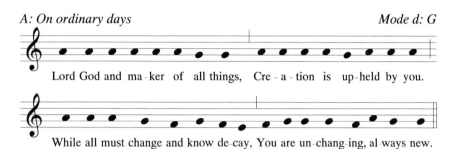

Lord God and ma-ker of all things, Cre - a - tion is up-held by you.

While all must change and know de-cay, You are un-chang-ing, al-ways new.

B: On lesser feast days   *Mode 8: F*

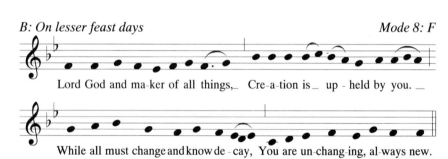

Lord God and ma-ker of all things,_ Cre-a-tion is_ up - held by you. _

While all must change and know de - cay, You are un-chang-ing, al-ways new.

C: On feast days   *Mode 8: G*

Lord God and ma-ker of __ all _ things, Cre-a-tion is up held _ by _ you.

While all must change and know de - cay, You are un-chang-ing, al - ways new.

MIDDAY PRAYER (SEXT)

Second tune   SAINT CROSS

1   Lord God and maker of all things,
       Creation is upheld by you.
       While all must change and perish here,
       You are unchanging, always new.

2   You are our solace and our shield,
       Our rock secure on which to build;
       You are the spirit's tranquil home,
       In you alone is hope fulfilled.

3   To God the Father and the Son
       And Holy Spirit render praise,
       Blest Trinity, from age to age,
       The strength of all our living days.

Text: Stanbrook Abbey. Second tune: John Bacchus Dykes (1823-76), altered.
Text: © 1974 and 1995, Stanbrook Abbey, Callow End, Worcester WR2 4TD.

239

First tunes

LITTLE HOURS

A: On ordinary days   *Mode d: C*

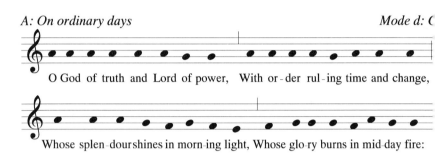

O God of truth and Lord of power, With or-der rul-ing time and change,

Whose splen-dour shines in morn-ing light, Whose glo-ry burns in mid-day fire:

B: On lesser feast days   *Mode 8:*

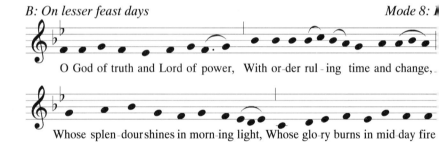

O God of truth and Lord of power, With or-der rul-ing time and change,

Whose splen-dour shines in morn-ing light, Whose glo-ry burns in mid-day fire

C: On feast days   *Mode 8: G*

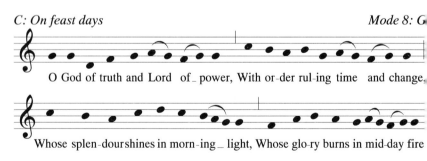

O God of truth and Lord of _ power, With or-der rul-ing time and change,

Whose splen-dour shines in morn-ing _ light, Whose glo-ry burns in mid-day fire

Text: Saint Mary's Abbey, West Malling; from *Rector potens verax Deus*, Saint Ambrose? (c. 339-397)
Second tune: Sandys' Psalm 8; melody and bass, Henry Lawes (1596-1662).

Text: © 1995, Saint Mary's Abbey, West Malling, Kent ME19 6JX.

Second tune   WHITEHALL (SANDYS' PSALM 8)

1   O God of truth and Lord of power,
    With order ruling time and change,
    Whose splendour shines in morning light,
    Whose glory burns in midday fire:

2   Extinguish every flame of strife
    And banish every wrong desire;
    Grant health of body and of mind,
    Create in us true peace of heart.

3   To God the Father glory be,
    All glory to his only Son
    And to the Spirit, Paraclete,
    In time and in eternity.

240   LM

First tunes   LITTLE HOURS

A: On ordinary days   *Mode d: G*

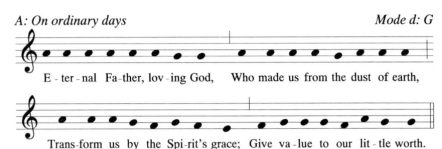

E - ter - nal Fa - ther, lov - ing God,   Who made us from the dust of earth,

Trans-form us by the Spi-rit's grace; Give va - lue to our lit - tle worth.

B: On lesser feast days   *Mode 8: F*

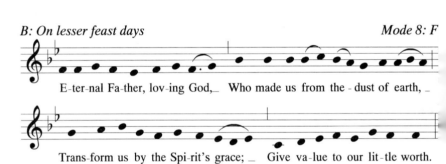

E - ter-nal Fa-ther, lov-ing God,__ Who made us from the - dust of earth, __

Trans-form us by the Spi-rit's grace; __ Give va-lue to our lit-tle worth.

C: On feast days   *Mode 8: G*

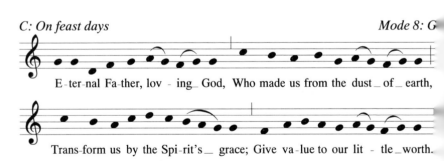

E - ter-nal Fa-ther, lov - ing__ God, Who made us from the dust _ of _ earth,

Trans-form us by the Spi-rit's __ grace; Give va-lue to our lit - tle __ worth.

Text: Stanbrook Abbey; from *Rerum Deus tenax vigor*, Saint Ambrose? (c. 339-397). Second tune melody: *Christliches Gesangbuchlein*, 1568; harmony, A. Gregory Murray OSB (1905-92).

MIDDAY PRAYER (NONE)

Second tune   SAXONY

1   Eternal Father, loving God,
     Who made us from the dust of earth,
     Transform us by the Spirit's grace;
     Give value to our little worth.

2   Prepare for us that day of days
     When Christ from heaven will come with might
     To call us out of dust again,
     Our bodies glorified in light.

3   O Godhead, here untouched, unseen,
     All things created bear your trace;
     The seed of glory sown in us
     Will flower when we see your face.

241 CM

First tune *Mode 3: E*

VAVASOUR

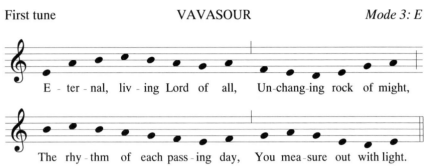

E - ter - nal, liv - ing Lord of all, Un-chang-ing rock of might,

The rhy - thm of each pass - ing day, You mea - sure out with light.

Second tune

OUDE KERK

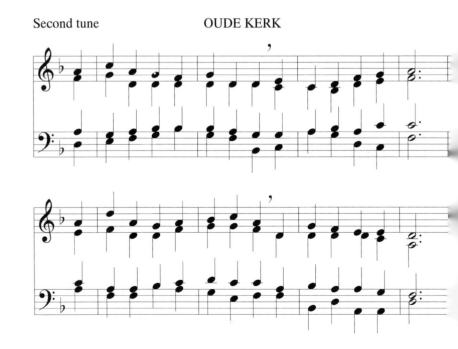

MIDDAY PRAYER (NONE)

1   Eternal, living Lord of all,
     Unchanging rock of might,
     The rhythm of each passing day
     You measure out with light.

2   We pray that evening may be calm,
     And life may never fail;
     Through death may we in glory find
     A peace that will prevail.

3   Most holy Father, grant our prayer
     Through Christ your only Son,
     That in your Spirit we may live
     And praise you ever One.

Text: Ralph Wright OSB, altered; from *Rerum Deus tenax vigor*, Saint Ambrose? (c. 339-397). First tune: Stanbrook Abbey. Second tune: melody, Dutch traditional; harmony, John Harper.

Text: © 1989, GIA Publications Inc., 7404 South Mason Avenue, Chicago, Illinois 60638. All rights reserved. First tune: © 1974, Stanbrook Abbey, Callow End, Worcester WR2 4TD. Second tune (harmony): © 1995, Panel of Monastic Musicians, Mount Saint Bernard Abbey, Coalville, Leicester LE67 5UL.

242

First tune   **MAGNAE DEUS**   *Mode 2: F*

O gra-cious light, Lord Je-sus Christ, In you the Fa-ther's glo - ry shone.

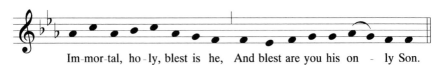

Im-mor-tal, ho-ly, blest is he, And blest are you his on - ly Son.

Second tune   **SOLOTHURN**

EVENING PRAYER

1   O gracious light, Lord Jesus Christ,
    In you the Father's glory shone.
    Immortal, holy, blest is he,
    And blest are you his only Son.

2   Now sunset comes, but light shines forth,
    The lamps are lit to pierce the night.
    Praise Father, Son, and Spirit, God
    Who dwells in the eternal light.

3   Worthy are you of endless praise,
    O Son of God, life-giving Lord;
    Wherefore you are, through all the earth
    And in the highest heaven, adored.

Text: Francis Bland Tucker (1895-1984); from *Phos Hilaron*, Athenogenes? (2nd century). Second tune: melody, Swiss traditional; harmony: Ralph Vaughan Williams (1872-1958), from *The English Hymnal*, altered.

243

11.6.11.4

First tune INGLEBY

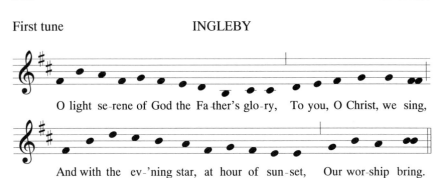

O light se-rene of God the Fa-ther's glo-ry, To you, O Christ, we sing,

And with the ev-'ning star, at hour of sun-set, Our wor-ship bring.

Second tune PHOS HILARON

PHOS HILARON II **243**

1   O light serene of God the Father's glory,
      To you, O Christ, we sing,
      And with the evening star, at hour of sunset,
      Our worship bring.

2   To Father, Son and God's most Holy Spirit,
      Eternal praise is due.
      O Christ, who gave your life, the world gives glory
      And thanks to you.

Text: Stanbrook Abbey; from *Phos Hilaron*, Athenogenes? (2nd century). First tune: Stanbrook Abbey. Second tune: melody, Alan Rees OSB; harmony, John Harper.

Text and first tune: © 1974, Stanbrook Abbey, Callow End, Worcester WR2 4TD. Second tune: melody, © 1995, Belmont Abbey Trustees, Hereford, HR2 9RZ; harmony, © 1995, Panel of Monastic Musicians, Mount Saint Bernard Abbey, Coalville, Leicester LE67 5UL.

244 8.7.8.7

First tune NEATH *Mode 4: F♯*

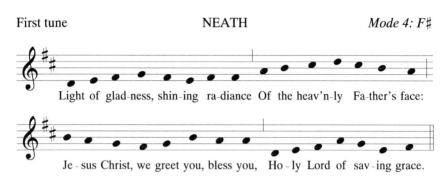

Light of glad-ness, shin-ing ra-diance Of the heav'n-ly Fa-ther's face:

Je - sus Christ, we greet you, bless you, Ho - ly Lord of sav-ing grace.

Second tune SUSSEX

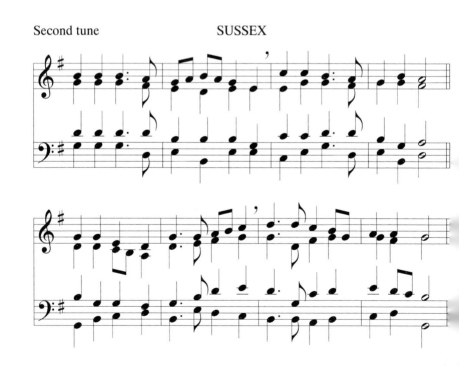

EVENING PRAYER

1   Light of gladness, shining radiance
       Of the heavenly Father's face:
       Jesus Christ, we greet you, bless you,
       Holy Lord of saving grace.

2   As the day draws near its ending
       Sunlight dims with fading rays;
       To the Father, Son and Spirit
       Now we sing our song of praise.

3   Son of God, the world's redeemer,
       Endless praises are your due;
       Lord of life, may all creation
       Bring its joyful thanks to you.

Text: Saint Dominic's Convent, Stone; from *Phos Hilaron*, Athenogenes? (2nd century). First tune: Mount Saint Bernard Abbey. Second tune: English traditional melody, adapted and arranged by Ralph Vaughan Williams (1872-1958), from *The English Hymnal*.

245 LM

First tune   O LUX, BEATA TRINITAS   *Mode 8: G*

O _____ blest _____ cre - a - tor, God _____ most high,

Great _____ ru - ler of the star - filled sky,

You clothe the _____ day with _____ ra - diant _____ light,

In sha - dows dark en - fold _____ the night.

Second tune   SOLOTHURN

EVENING PRAYER

1   O blest creator, God most high,
     Great ruler of the star-filled sky,
     You clothe the day with radiant light,
     In shadows dark enfold the night.

2   We thank you for this day now gone;
     And pray you, as the night draws on,
     Help us, your children, thus to raise
     Our evening offering of praise.

3   To you our hearts their music bring,
     To you our gathered voices sing;
     To you our hearts' deep longings soar,
     And you our chastened souls adore.

4   O Christ, the Father's only Son,
     And Spirit of them both, but One;
     God over all, whom all obey,
     Shield us, great Trinity, we pray.

J. D. Chambers (1805-93), altered and abbreviated; from *Deus, creator omnium*, Saint Ambrose (c. 339-397). Second tune: melody, Swiss traditional; harmony, Ralph Vaughan Williams (1872-1958), from *The English Hymnal*, altered.

246

LM

First tune

LUCIS CREATOR OPTIME

Mode 8: E♭

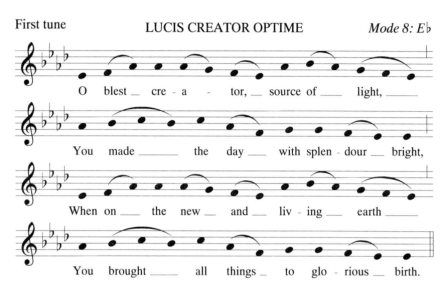

O blest __ cre - a - tor, __ source of ___ light, ___

You made _____ the day __ with splen - dour __ bright,

When on ___ the new __ and __ liv - ing __ earth _____

You brought _____ all things _ to glo - rious _ birth.

Second tune

LUCIS CREATOR

EVENING PRAYER

1   O blest creator, source of light,
    You made the day with splendour bright,
    When on the new and living earth
    You brought all things to glorious birth.

2   You joined the morn and evening ray;
    You called it good and named it day.
    But now the threatening darkness nears,
    We pray you, Father, calm our fears;

3   Lest we, beset by doubt and strife,
    Forget your blessed gift of life,
    And languishing in mind distressed,
    Be crushed by guilt, by sin oppressed.

4   Eternal Father, help us rise
    And run to gain the heavenly prize;
    For you alone can make us strong
    To turn from sin and cease from wrong.

5   Defend us, Father, through the night,
    And with your Son and Spirit bright,
    The Trinity whom we adore,
    Be with us now and evermore.

Text: Anne K. Le Croy, altered; from *Lucis creator optime*. Second tune: melody, Angers, 17th century; harmony, editors.

Text: © 1982, Church Hymnal Corporation, 445 Fifth Avenue, New York, NY 10016. Second tune (harmony): © 1995, Panel of Monastic Musicians, Mount Saint Bernard Abbey, Coalville, Leicester LE67 5UL.

247 LM

First tune   IMMENSE CAELI CONDITOR (i)   *Mode 1: E*

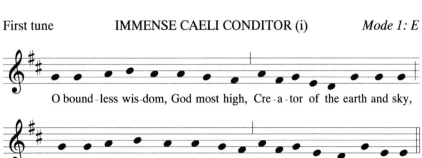

O bound-less wis-dom, God most high, Cre-a-tor of the earth and sky,

With rush-ing streams and glist'n-ing rain All liv-ing crea-tures you sus-tain.

Second tune   UFFINGHAM

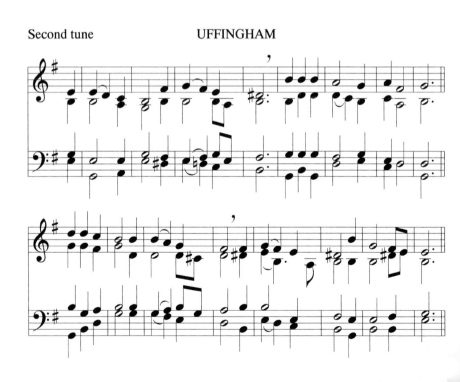

EVENING PRAYER

1 O boundless wisdom, God most high,
  Creator of the earth and sky,
  With rushing streams and glistening rain
  All living creatures you sustain.

2 So pour on us, who seek your face,
  The waters of your quickening grace;
  Renew the source of life within,
  Wash from our souls the stain of sin.

3 Let faith discern the eternal light
  Beyond the darkness of the night,
  That through the glass we darkly see
  The way of truth which sets us free.

4 To God the Father, God the Son,
  And God the Spirit, ever One,
  All honour, praise and glory be
  From age to age eternally.

Text: editors' compilation; from *Immense caeli conditor*, Saint Gregory? (c. 540-604). Second tune: Jeremiah Clarke (c. 1673-1707).

Text: © 1995, Panel of Monastic Musicians, Mount Saint Bernard Abbey, Coalville, Leicester LE67 5UL.

248 LM

First tune IMMENSE CAELI CONDITOR (ii) *Mode d: G*

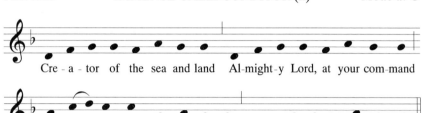

Cre - a - tor of the sea and land Al-might-y Lord, at your com-mand

The stor - my deeps give way to earth, A sign of com-ing life and birth.

Second tune EISENACH

EVENING PRAYER

1   Creator of the sea and land
    Almighty Lord, at your command
    The stormy deeps give way to earth,
    A sign of coming life and birth.

2   Each living branch, each fruit and seed
    Tells in itself a godly deed:
    The green trees blossom and fulfil,
    In bearing fruit, your perfect will.

3   Lord, heal the wounds through sin sustained,
    That we in faith and hope regained,
    May find for penance true a place
    And know the strength and life of grace.

4   May every soul your law obey
    And keep from every evil way,
    Rejoice each promised good to win
    And flee from every mortal sin.

5   To God the Father, God the Son,
    And God the Spirit, ever One,
    All honour, praise and glory be
    From age to age eternally.

Text: editors' compilation; from *Telluris ingens conditor*, Saint Gregory? (c. 540-604). melody, J. H. Schein (1586-1630); harmony, editors.

Text and second tune (harmony): © 1995, Panel of Monastic Musicians, Mount Saint Bernard Abbey, Coalville, Leicester LE67 5UL.

249

First tune   **MAGNAE DEUS**   *Mode 2: F*

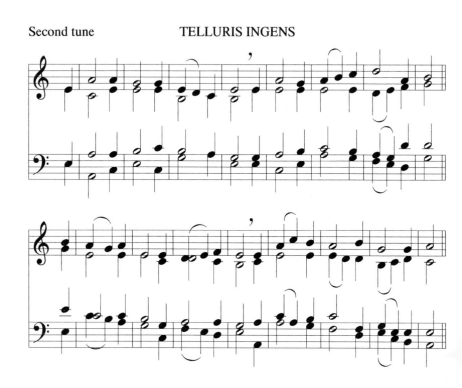

O God, whose hand has spread the sky With all its shin-ing hosts on high,

You, when the fourth day was be-gun, Did shape the cir-cle of_the sun.

Second tune   **TELLURIS INGENS**

EVENING PRAYER

1   O God, whose hand has spread the sky
       With all its shining hosts on high,
       You, when the fourth day was begun,
       Did shape the circle of the sun.

2   Endowing it with fiery light,
       You crowned the sun with royal might,
       And set the moon her ordered ways
       To mark and govern months and days.

3   Shed forth your truth, O fount of light,
       In Christ the way lead us aright;
       As children bright with your new fire,
       Come, Lord, fulfil our hearts' desire.

4   To God the Father, God the Son,
       And God the Spirit, ever One,
       All honour, praise and glory be
       From age to age eternally.

xt: Gethsemani Abbey, altered; from *Caeli Deus sanctissime*, Saint Gregory? (c. 540-604). Second
ne: Alan Rees OSB.

xt: © 1975, Gethsemani Abbey, 3642 Monks Road, Trappist, Kentucky 40051. Second tune: © 1995,
lmont Abbey Trustees, Hereford, HR2 9RZ.

250   10.6.10.6

BUILDWAS   *Mode 6: F*

Ma-ker of all, at whose word the great stars Come to birth and then die;

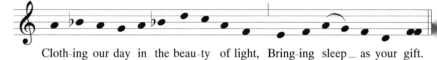

Cloth-ing our day in the beau-ty of light, Bring-ing sleep — as your gift.

EVENING PRAYER

1   Maker of all, at whose word the great stars
     Come to birth and then die,
     Clothing our day in the beauty of light,
     Bringing sleep as your gift.

2   Day is now done, and as evening draws on
     We give thanks for your care;
     Come to our aid as we sing in your praise
     And give voice to our love.

3   Deep in the heart may our song find its source,
     On our lips sound with joy.
     You are the one whom our love would embrace,
     Whom our soul would adore.

4   Night will enshroud us in darkness and gloom
     And the daylight will fade;
     Kindle within us the light of our faith
     To make night clear as day.

5   Lull now to rest all our sinful desires
     While the soul stays alert.
     Faith is the source of untroubled repose
     To the hearts that are pure.

6   Come, let us pray to the Father and Christ,
     To the Spirit of both:
     Three who are One in unwearying might
     And in tenderest love.

Text: Mount Saint Bernard Abbey, abbreviated; from *Deus, creator omnium*, Saint Ambrose (c. 339-97). Tune: Mount Saint Bernard Abbey.

Text and tune: © 1995, Mount Saint Bernard Abbey, Coalville, Leicester LE67 5UL.

251

First tune **IMMENSE CAELI CONDITOR (i)** *Mode 1: E*

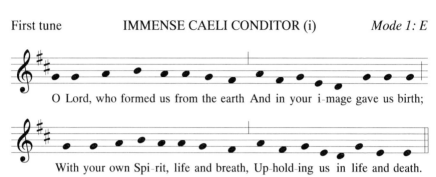

O Lord, who formed us from the earth And in your i-mage gave us birth;

With your own Spi-rit, life and breath, Up-hold-ing us in life and death.

Second tune **AUCTORITATE SAECULI**

EVENING PRAYER

1   O Lord, who formed us from the earth
    And in your image gave us birth;
    With your own Spirit, life and breath,
    Upholding us in life and death.

2   When in the cool of day you came,
    Commanding that the beasts be named;
    From sleeping Adam's open side
    Created Eve to be his bride.

3   Both male and female, flesh and bone,
    On earth your very image own.
    And joined again, one flesh to be,
    They tell a future mystery.

4   From Christ the second Adam's side
    Is born the Church, his cherished bride;
    To share Christ's toil, his joy and pain,
    In Paradise to share his reign.

5   To God the Father, God the Son,
    And God the Spirit, ever One,
    All honour, praise and glory be
    From age to age eternally.

ext: Gethsemani Abbey, altered; from *Plasmator hominis Deus*, Saint Gregory? (c. 540-604). Second ne: melody, Poitiers Antiphoner, 1746; harmony, editors.

ext: © 1975, Gethsemani Abbey, 3642 Monks Road, Trappist, Kentucky 40051. Second tune (harmony): 1995, Panel of Monastic Musicians, Mount Saint Bernard Abbey, Coalville, Leicester LE67 5UL.

252

First tune   O LUX, BEATA TRINITAS   *Mode 8: G*

O ____ Tri - ni - ty of bless - ed light,

O ____ u - ni - ty of pri - mal might,

As now the ____ fie - ry ____ sun ____ de - parts,

So shed ____ your ra - diance in ____ our hearts.

Second tune   **SOLOTHURN**

EVENING PRAYER

1   O Trinity of blessed light,
     O unity of primal might,
     As now the fiery sun departs,
     So shed your radiance in our hearts.

2   To you our morning song of praise
     To you our evening prayer we raise:
     May we behold your glorious face,
     And joy in your eternal grace.

3   To God the Father, God the Son,
     And God the Spirit, praise be done;
     To you most holy Trinity,
     Praise now and for eternity.

Text: John Mason Neale, altered; from *O lux beata Trinitas* (Ambrosian, 7th or 8th century). Second tune: melody, Swiss traditional; harmony, Ralph Vaughan Williams (1872-1958), from *The English Hymnal*, altered.

Text (this version): © 1995, Panel of Monastic Musicians, Mount Saint Bernard Abbey, Coalville, Leicester LE67 5UL. Second tune (harmony): © Oxford University Press. Altered by permission.

253   LM

First tune   **LUCIS CREATOR OPTIME**   *Mode 8: E♭*

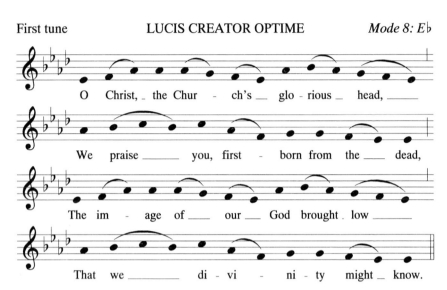

O Christ, the Church's glorious head,
We praise you, first - born from the dead,
The im - age of our God brought low
That we di - vi - ni - ty might know.

Second tune   **LUCIS CREATOR**

EVENING PRAYER

1   O Christ, the Church's glorious head,
    We praise you, first-born from the dead,
    The image of our God brought low
    That we divinity might know.

2   Through you and for you, at God's word,
    The formless depths to life were stirred;
    All things in heaven and on earth,
    All sovereignties have come to birth.

3   In you God's fulness came to dwell,
    That love might Satan's hold repel,
    And by your death upon the tree
    You loosed us from captivity.

4   To God the Father, God the Son,
    And God the Spirit, Three in One;
    To you, O blessed Trinity,
    Be praise in all eternity.

ext: Community of Saint Mary the Virgin, Wantage, altered. Second tune: melody, Angers, 17th century; armony, editors.

ext: © 1995, Community of Saint Mary the Virgin, Wantage, Oxfordshire. Second tune (harmony): © 95, Panel of Monastic Musicians, Mount Saint Bernard Abbey, Coalville, Leicester LE67 5UL.

254   LM

First tune   IMMENSE CAELI CONDITOR (ii)   *Mode d: G*

Lord Je - sus Christ, a - bide with us, Now that the sun has run its course;

Let hope_ be not ob-scured by night, But may faith's dark-ness be as light.

Second tune   CITEAUX

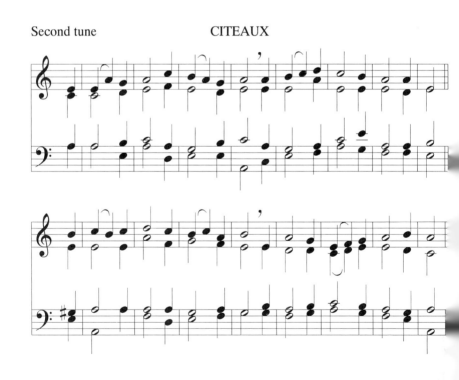

EVENING PRAYER

1   Lord Jesus Christ, abide with us,
    Now that the sun has run its course;
    Let hope be not obscured by night,
    But may faith's darkness be as light.

2   Lord Jesus Christ, grant us your peace,
    And when the trials of earth shall cease,
    Grant us the morning light of grace,
    The radiant splendour of your face.

3   Immortal, holy, threefold light,
    Yours be the kingdom, power, and might;
    All glory be eternally
    To you, life-giving Trinity.

Text: St Joseph's Abbey, Spencer, Massachusetts, altered; from *Ach, bleib bei uns,* Nikolaus Selnecker (1528-92). Second tune: Alan Rees OSB, harmony altered.

Text: © 1968, St Joseph's Abbey, Spencer, Massachusetts 01562. Second tune: © 1995, Belmont Abbey Trustees, Hereford, HR2 9RZ.

255

8.10.10.10.8

HOLMCULTREN

Mode 5: C

O bless - ed, un - cre - a - ted Light,

The tri - ple source whence springs all life on earth,

As now ___ the sun is sink - ing in the west

A - mid ___ the em - bers of an - o - ther day,

Shine ___ clear and strong with - in our hearts.

EVENING PRAYER

1 O blessed, uncreated Light,
  The triple source whence springs all life on earth,
  As now the sun is sinking in the west
  Amid the embers of another day,
  Shine clear and strong within our hearts.

2 With songs of praise upon our lips,
  We stand before you in the morning light;
  We call upon your name as evening falls:
  From age to age beyond the bounds of time,
  Let prayers ascend before your throne.

3 Let every living thing on earth
  Give glory to our Father and our God,
  And with him praise his one and only Son
  Together with the Spirit, advocate,
  Both now and in eternity.

Text: Mount Saint Bernard Abbey, altered; from *O lux beata Trinitas* (Ambrosian, 7th or 8th century).
Tune: Mount Saint Bernard Abbey.

Text and tune: © 1995, Mount Saint Bernard Abbey, Coalville, Leicester LE67 5UL.

256   11.11.11.5

First tune   O PATER SANCTE   *Mode 3: F♯*

Christ, migh - ty sav - iour, light of all cre - a - tion,

You make the day - time, ra - diant with the sun - light,

And to the night give glit-ter-ing a-dorn-ment, Stars in the hea-ven.

1   Christ, mighty saviour, light of all creation,
     You make the daytime, radiant with the sunlight,
     And to the night give glittering adornment,
     Stars in the heavens.

2   Now comes the day's end as the sun is setting:
     Mirror of daybreak, pledge of resurrection;
     While in the heavens choirs of stars appearing
     Hallow the nightfall.

3   Therefore we come our evening prayer to offer,
     Joyfully chanting holy hymns to praise you,
     With all creation joining hearts and voices
     Singing your glory.

4   Though bodies slumber, hearts shall keep their vigil,
     Forever resting in the peace of Jesus,
     In light or darkness worshipping our saviour
     Now and for ever.

Second tune HERR, DEINEN ZORN

Text: Alan G. McDougall (1895-1964), revised Anne K. Le Croy and others; from *Christe, lux mundi* (Mozarabic, 10th century). Second tune: melody adapted from Johann Crüger (1598-1662); harmony, Richard Dubois, altered.

Text: © 1982, Church Hymnal Corporation, 445 Fifth Avenue, New York, NY 10016. Second tune (harmony): © 1972, Richard Dubois; by permission of Paul Inwood.

257

First tune   **MAGNAE DEUS**   *Mode 2: F*

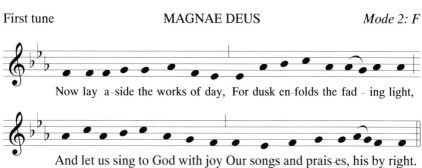

Now lay a-side the works of day, For dusk en-folds the fad - ing light,

And let us sing to God with joy Our songs and prais-es, his by right.

Second tune   **HERONGATE**

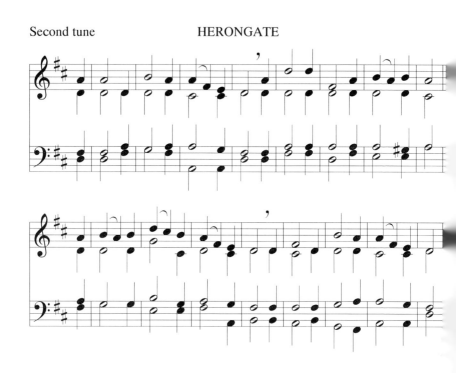

EVENING PRAYER

1   Now lay aside the works of day,
     For dusk enfolds the fading light,
     And let us sing to God with joy
     Our songs and praises, his by right.

2   Throughout the common, daily round
     Direct us in your ways, O Lord;
     May all who in your vineyard toil
     From you receive their great reward.

3   Lord Jesus Christ, you summoned us
     To press towards our recompense.
     Assist our labours, then grant rest
     When your great love shall call us hence.

4   O Christ our king and gracious Lord,
     Whom with the Father we adore,
     And Holy Spirit, Paraclete,
     One God, both now and evermore.

Text: editors' compilation; from *Horis peractis*. Second tune: melody, Essex folksong; collected and arranged by Ralph Vaughan Williams (1872-1958), from *The English Hymnal*.

Text: © 1995, Panel of Monastic Musicians, Mount Saint Bernard Abbey, Coalville, Leicester LE67 UL. Second tune: © Oxford University Press.

258 LM

First tune   IMMENSE CAELI CONDITOR (i)   *Mode 1: E*

Our Lord and ma-ker, from your throne You fa-shion all things, God a-lone;

At your de-cree the liv-ing earth To crea-tures great and small gives birth.

Second tune   DU MEINER SEELEN (ANGELUS)

EVENING PRAYER

1   Our Lord and maker, from your throne
     You fashion all things, God alone;
     At your decree the living earth
     To creatures great and small gives birth.

2   The many forms that fill the land,
     Imbued with life at your command,
     Are given to us, each in its place,
     And serving, praise you for your grace.

3   From all your servants drive away
     Whatever sinful thoughts today
     Disturbed the intentions of the heart,
     Or in our actions claimed their part.

4   To God the Father, God the Son
     And God the Spirit, ever One,
     All honour, praise and glory be
     From age to age eternally.

ext: editors' compilation; from *Plasmator hominis Deus*, Saint Gregory? (c. 540-604) Second tune: *antica Spiritualia*, 1847; based on a melody by G. Joseph, 1657.

ext: © 1995, Panel of Monastic Musicians, Mount Saint Bernard Abbey, Coalville, Leicester LE67 JL.

259

First tune   **CANTON**   *Mode 2: F*

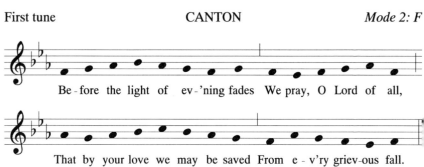

Be - fore the light of ev -'ning fades We pray, O Lord of all,

That by your love we may be saved From e - v'ry griev-ous fall.

Second tune   **TALLIS' ORDINAL**

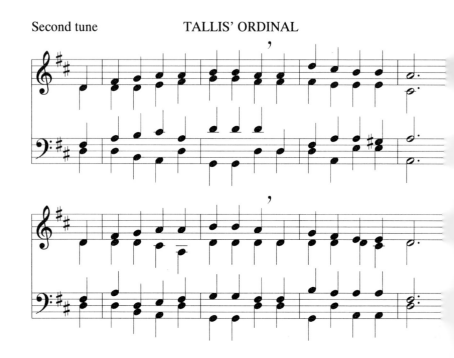

COMPLINE

1   Before the light of evening fades
     We pray, O Lord of all,
     That by your love we may be saved
     From every grievous fall.

2   Repel the terrors of the night
     And Satan's power of guile;
     Impose a calm and restful sleep
     That nothing may defile.

3   Most holy Father, hear our prayer
     Through Christ your only Son,
     That in your Spirit we may live
     And praise you, ever One.

ext: Ralph Wright OSB; from *Te lucis ante terminum* (5th or 6th century). First tune: Laurence Bévenot
SB (1901-90). Second tune: Thomas Tallis (c. 1505-85).

260 LM

First tunes   COMPLINE MELODIES (SALISBURY)

A: On Sundays and feastdays *Mode 8: F*

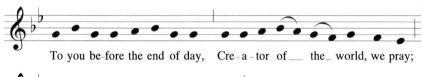

To you be-fore the end of day, Cre-a-tor of ___ the _ world, we pray;

In love un-fail - ing, hear our prayer, En-fold us in your watch-ful care.

B: On weekdays *Mode 8: E*

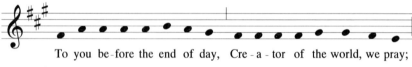

To you be-fore the end of day, Cre-a-tor of the world, we pray;

In love un-fail-ing, hear our prayer, En-fold us in your watch-ful care.

Alternatives: COMPLINE MELODIES, 261

Text: editors' compilation; from *Te lucis ante terminum* as revised in *Liber Hymnarius*. Second tun
Thomas Tallis (c. 1505-85).

SATURDAY (II)   **260**

Second tune   TALLIS' CANON

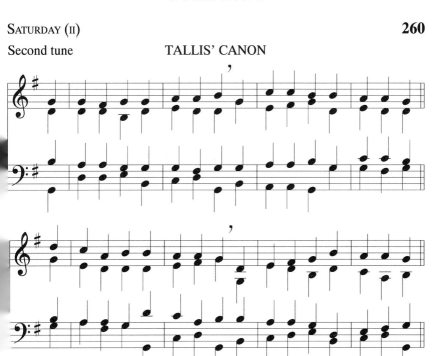

1   To you, before the end of day,
     Creator of the world, we pray;
     In love unfailing, hear our prayer,
     Enfold us in your watchful care.

2   Lord, when we sleep, be in our hearts,
     Your Spirit peace and rest imparts;
     Then, with the light of dawn, may we
     Your glory praise unendingly.

3   Your living power breathe from above,
     Renew in us the fire of love;
     And may your brightness drive away
     All darkness in eternal day.

4   O Father, hear us, through your Son,
     Who, with the Spirit, ever One
     Now reigns as living Trinity
     In time and for eternity.

261

LM

First tunes   COMPLINE MELODIES

A: On Sundays   *Mode 8: G*

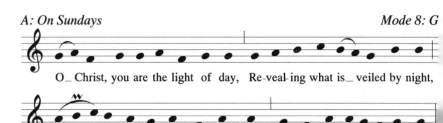

O_ Christ, you are the light of day, Re-veal-ing what is_ veiled by night,

The _ morn-ing star that gives the pledge, And pro-mise of e-ter-nal light.

B: On feastdays   *Mode 2: A*

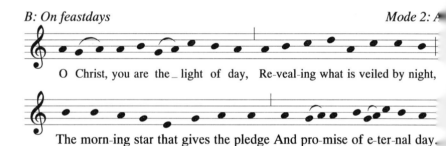

O Christ, you are the _ light of day, Re-veal-ing what is veiled by night,

The morn-ing star that gives the pledge And pro-mise of e-ter-nal day.

Alternatives: COMPLINE MELODIES (SALISBURY), 260

> 1   O Christ, you are the light of day,
>   Revealing what is veiled by night,
>   The morning star that gives the pledge
>   And promise of eternal light.
>
> 2   Watch over us who love you well,
>   And when our eyes are closed in sleep,
>   Protected by your strong right hand,
>   With you, our hearts will vigil keep.
>
> 3   O Father, Son and Spirit blest,
>   Immortal Trinity we praise,
>   Give us true sorrow for our sins
>   And life in everlasting days.

COMPLINE

Second tune   TALLIS' CANON

Text: Stanbrook Abbey; from *Christe, qui lux es et dies* (5th or 6th century). Second tune: Thomas Tallis (c. 1505-85).

Text: © 1974 and 1995, Stanbrook Abbey, Callow End, Worcester WR2 4TD.

262

First tune · **MALLING** · *Mode 4: F♯*

We praise you, Fa-ther, for your gift Of dusk and night-fall o-ver earth, ___

Fore-sha - dow-ing the mys-ter - y Of death that leads to end-less day. ___

Second tune · **NYMPHSFIELD**

COMPLINE

1   We praise you, Father, for your gift
         Of dusk and nightfall over earth,
         Foreshadowing the mystery
         Of death that leads to endless day.

2   Within your hands we rest secure;
         In quiet sleep our strength renew;
         Yet give your people hearts that wake
         In love to you, unsleeping Lord.

3   Your glory may we ever seek
         In rest, as in activity,
         Until its fulness is revealed,
         O source of life, O Trinity.

Text and first tune: Saint Mary's Abbey, West Malling. Second tune: melody, Charles Watson OSB; harmony, John Harper.

Text and first tune: © 1995, Saint Mary's Abbey, West Malling, Kent ME19 6JX. Second tune: melody, © 1995, Charles Watson OSB, Prinknash Abbey, Cranham, Gloucester GL4 8EX.; harmony, © 1995, Panel of Monastic Musicians, Mount Saint Bernard Abbey, Coalville, Leicester LE67 5UL.

263   8.7.8.7

First tune   **CULTOR DEI**   *Mode 8: F*

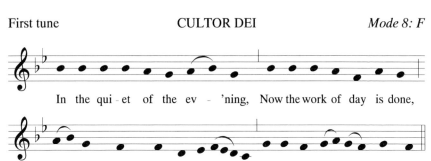

In the qui - et of the ev - - 'ning, Now the work of day is done,

Turn our thoughts, most lov-ing Fa - ther To the work of _ Christ, your Son.

Second tune   **WORTH**

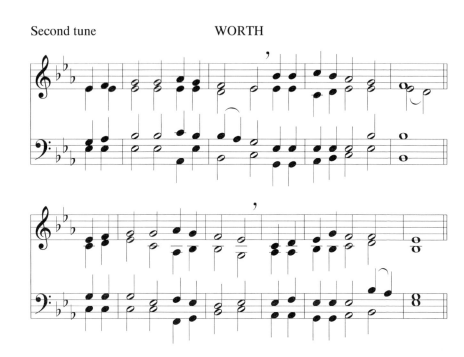

COMPLINE

1   In the quiet of the evening,
     Now the work of day is done,
     Turn our thoughts, most loving Father
     To the work of Christ, your Son.

2   In our wandering we have travelled
     Far from you throughout the day,
     Yet forgiving all, you sent us
     Christ to lead us, Christ the way.

3   When our ignorance is danger,
     Or we credit worldly lies,
     Then, with timely care, you give us
     Christ the truth to make us wise.

4   As the light of day is fading,
     Father, keep us in your sight;
     Pierce the dark of sin with splendour
     Shining out from Christ the light.

5   Glory be to God the Father,
     Glory be to God the Son,
     Glory to the Holy Spirit,
     Glory to the Three in One.

Text: Patrick Lee. Second tune: Philip Gaisford OSB, harmony adapted.

Text: © 1987, Patrick Lee, 8 Hampton Fields, Oswestry, Shropshire SY11 1TJ. Second tune: © 1988, Worth Abbey Music, Crawley, West Sussex RH10 4SB.

264   10.10

First tune   DAYSTAR   *Mode 1: C*

Lord may your love be with us while we sleep,

And your strong care our souls and bo - dies keep.

Second tune   SONG 46

COMPLINE

1   Lord may your love be with us while we sleep,
        And your strong care our souls and bodies keep.

2   Lord may your truth inform our minds always,
        And may your spirit turn our night to day.

3   Lord may your peace be in our hearts held fast,
        Bring us in safety home to you at last.

Text: Society of the Sacred Mission. First tune: Saint Dominic's Convent, Stone. Second tune: melody and bass, Orlando Gibbons (1583-1625).

Text: © 1995, Society of the Sacred Mission, Willen Priory, Milton Keynes, Buckinghamshire. First tune: © 1995, Saint Dominic's Convent, Stone, Staffordshire ST15 8EN.

265 8.4.8.4.8.8.8.4

First tune DAY IS DONE *Mode 1: D*

Day is done, but love un-fail-ing Dwells__ e-ver here;

Sha-dows fall but hope pre-vail-ing Calms__ e-v'ry fear.

Lov-ing Fa-ther, none for-sak-ing, Take our hearts, of love's own mak-ing,

Watch our sleep-ing, guard our wak-ing, Be al-ways near.

1   Day is done, but love unfailing
     Dwells ever here;
     Shadows fall, but hope prevailing
     Calms every fear.
     Loving Father, none forsaking,
     Take our hearts, of Love's own making,
     Watch our sleeping, guard our waking,
     Be always near.

2   Dark descends, but light unending
     Shines through our night;
     You are with us, ever lending
     New strength to sight;
     One in love, your truth confessing,
     One in hope of heaven's blessing,
     May we see, in Love's possessing,
     Love's endless light.

Text: James Quinn SJ. First tune: Alan Rees OSB. Second tune: melody, Welsh traditional; harmony attributed to Ralph Vaughan Williams (1872-1958).

Text: © 1969, James Quinn SJ and Geoffrey Chapman, a Cassell imprint, Wellington House, Strand London WC2R 0BB. First tune: © Belmont Abbey Trustees, Hereford HR2 9RZ.

COMPLINE

Second tune · · · · · · · · · AR HYD Y NOS

3   Eyes will close, but you, unsleeping,
Watch by our side;
Death may come; in Love's safe keeping
Still we abide.
God of love, all evil quelling,
Sin forgiving, fear dispelling,
Stay with us, our hearts indwelling,
This eventide.

266

7.6.7.6

First tune

LAURENTIUS

Mode 2: G

Now at the day‑light's end‑ing We turn, O God, to you:

Send forth your Ho‑ly Spi‑rit, Our spi‑rit now re‑new.

Second tune

DU FONDS DE MA PENSÉE

COMPLINE

1   Now at the daylight's ending
    We turn, O God, to you:
    Send forth your Holy Spirit,
    Our spirit now renew.

2   To you in adoration,
    In thankfulness and praise,
    In faith and hope and gladness,
    Our loving hearts we raise.

3   With watchful eyes, O shepherd,
    Look down upon your sheep;
    Stretch forth your hands in healing
    And close our eyes in sleep.

4   Come down, O Holy Spirit,
    To be our loving guest;
    Be near us, holy angels,
    And guard us as we rest.

5   We praise you, heavenly Father:
    From you all light descends;
    You give us heaven's glory
    When life's brief daylight ends.

6   We praise you, Jesus, saviour,
    The light of heaven above;
    We praise you, Holy Spirit,
    The living flame of love.

Text: James Quinn SJ, abbreviated. First tune: Laurence Bévenot OSB. Second tune: melody, Strasburg, 1539, abbreviated; harmony, Louis Bourgeois (c. 1510-61).

Text: © 1969, James Quinn SJ and Geoffrey Chapman, a Cassell imprint, Wellington House, Strand, London WC2R 0BB. First tune: © 1995, Ampleforth Abbey Trust, York YO6 4EN.

Ω

THE COMMON

301-343

301 8.7.8.7.8.7

First tune ANGULARIS *Mode 4: E*

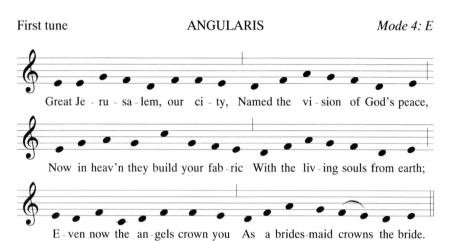

Great Je - ru - sa - lem, our ci - ty, Named the vi - sion of God's peace,

Now in heav'n they build your fab - ric With the liv - ing souls from earth;

E - ven now the an - gels crown you As a brides-maid crowns the bride.

Alternatives: URBS IERUSALEM BEATA, 304; GALLI CANTU, 339

Text: Mount Saint Bernard Abbey, altered; from *Urbs Ierusalem beata* (8th or 9th centuries). First tune: Mount Saint Bernard Abbey.

Text and first tune: © 1995, Mount Saint Bernard Abbey, Coalville, Leicester LE67 5UL.

THE DEDICATION OF A CHURCH

1   Great Jerusalem, our city,
     Named the vision of God's peace,
     Now in heaven they build your fabric
     With the living souls from earth;
     Even now the angels crown you
     As a bridesmaid crowns the bride

2   Fresh from heaven's bridal chamber
     As a bride she comes from God,
     In her youth prepared and ready
     For her marriage with the Lord;
     All her streets, her walls and ramparts
     Fashioned from the purest gold.

3   All her gates with pearls are gleaming,
     All her gateways open wide,
     Welcoming and calling homeward
     Those who for the love of Christ
     In this world have drunk his chalice,
     Meriting his own reward.

4   All her stones are bruised and hammered,
     Polished, carved to perfect form,
     Truly laid by craft of builder,
     Each in its appointed place;
     Planned, foreseen to stand for ever
     In the temple walls of God.

5   Glory give to God and honour,
     Always, everywhere, most high,
     Father and the Son together
     With the glorious Paraclete;
     Theirs be power and theirs be worship
     Now through all eternity.

301   8.7.8.7.8.7

Second tune   ORIEL

Alternative: FORTUNATUS NEW, 304

Text: Mount Saint Bernard Abbey, altered; from *Urbs Ierusalem beata* (8th or 9th centuries). Second tune: C. Ett, *Cantica Sacra,* Munich 1840.

Text: © 1995, Mount Saint Bernard Abbey, Coalville, Leicester LE67 5UL.

THE DEDICATION OF A CHURCH

1   Great Jerusalem, our city,
     Named the vision of God's peace,
     Now in heaven they build your fabric
     With the living souls from earth;
     Even now the angels crown you
     As a bridesmaid crowns the bride

2   Fresh from heaven's bridal chamber
     As a bride she comes from God,
     In her youth prepared and ready
     For her marriage with the Lord;
     All her streets, her walls and ramparts
     Fashioned from the purest gold.

3   All her gates with pearls are gleaming,
     All her gateways open wide,
     Welcoming and calling homeward
     Those who for the love of Christ
     In this world have drunk his chalice,
     Meriting his own reward.

4   All her stones are bruised and hammered,
     Polished, carved to perfect form,
     Truly laid by craft of builder,
     Each in its appointed place;
     Planned, foreseen to stand for ever
     In the temple walls of God.

5   Glory give to God and honour,
     Always, everywhere, most high,
     Father and the Son together
     With the glorious Paraclete;
     Theirs be power and theirs be worship
     Now through all eternity.

302 11.11.11.5

First tune **STROUD GREEN** *Mode 1: D*

Christ,_ the e - ter - nal Lord of all cre - a - tion,

Hear _ now your ser - vants as they with de - vot - ion,

E - ver your child - ren, year by year re - joic - ing,

Chant in your tem - ple.

Alternative: WANTAGE, 303

1 Christ, the eternal Lord of all creation,
   Hear now your servants as they with devotion,
   Ever your children, year by year rejoicing,
   Chant in your temple.

2 Hallowed this dwelling of our king almighty:
   It is none other than the gate of heaven;
   Strangers and pilgrims, seeking life unending,
   Pass through its portals.

3 This is your temple; here your people gather,
   Ever enriched by sacramental feasting;
   Grant us, we pray you, when this life is ended
   Heaven eternal.

Second tune CHRISTE SANCTORUM

Text: Farnborough Abbey, altered. First tune: Anthony Greening. Second tune: melody, Paris Antiphoner, 1681; harmony, Ralph Vaughan Williams (1872-1958), from *The English Hymnal*.

First tune: © 1995, Elmore Abbey, Church Lane, Speen, Newbury, Berkshire RG13 1SA; by permission of the abbot and community. Second tune (harmony): © Oxford University Press.

303 11.11.11.5

First tune WANTAGE *Mode 1: D*

Je - sus our sav - iour, sov'-reign Lord of all things,

Hear the pe - ti - tions of your low - ly peo - ple,

Ga-thered to-ge - ther in this church to ho - nour Its de-di-ca - tion.

Alternative: STROUD GREEN, 302

1 Jesus our saviour, sovereign Lord of all things,
   Hear the petitions of your lowly people,
   Gathered together in this church to honour
   Its dedication.

2 Blest are these walls; their holiness surrounds us:
   This is God's temple and the gate of heaven,
   Open to welcome all who seek with longing
   Homeland eternal.

3 Here in this building we receive your treasures,
   Sacraments holy, giving grace and pardon,
   Christ's great oblation offers food that pledges
   Life everlasting.

4 So we implore you, holy God almighty,
   Bless and protect us with your loving favour,
   As we bear witness, with our prayer and praise
   In this your temple.

5 Praise to the Father, and to you, our saviour,
   King of all mercy, Lord throughout the ages,
   And to the Spirit, may our praise find echo
   All the world over.

Second tune   CHRISTE SANCTORUM

Text: Saint Cecilia's Abbey, Ryde, altered; from *Christe, cunctorum dominator alme* (7th century?).
First tune: Community of Saint Mary the Virgin. Second tune: melody, Paris Antiphoner, 1681; harmony,
Ralph Vaughan Williams (1872-1958), from *The English Hymnal.*

304 8.7.8.7.8.7

First tune URBS IERUSALEM BEATA *Mode 2: F*

Christ was sent, the true foun-da-tion, Christ, the on-ly cor-ner-stone,

Bond-ing well the walls to-ge - ther, Join-ing strong-ly all in one:

Ho-ly Zion in faith re-ceived him; In that faith she will en-dure.

Alternatives: ANGULARIS, 301; GALLI CANTU, 339

1 Christ was sent, the true foundation,
   Christ, the only corner-stone,
   Bonding well the walls together,
   Joining strongly all in one:
   Holy Zion in faith received him;
   In that faith she will endure.

2 Full of strong melodious praises,
   Echoing with joyful song,
   All this consecrated city,
   So beloved and dear to God,
   Fervently proclaims the Godhead:
   Persons Three in nature One.

3 God most high, when we entreat you
   In this temple, meet our need;
   And accept in loving goodness
   All the longing of our prayer;
   Constantly pour out your blessing
   Rich and full within these walls.

4 Hear our heartfelt intercession
   As we pray within this place;
   May we find the grace to enter
   Paradise when death shall come;
   May we know the peace of heaven
   With your saints for evermore.

5 Glory give to God and honour,
   Always, everywhere, most high,
   Father and the Son together
   With the glorious Paraclete:
   Theirs be power and theirs be worship
   Now through all eternity.

Second tune   FORTUNATUS NEW

Alternative: ORIEL, 301

Text: Mount Saint Bernard Abbey, altered; from *Angularis fundamentum* (8th or 9th century). Second tune: melody, Carl F. Schalk; harmony, John Harper.

305 6.6.6.6

First tune   **STELLA MARIS**   *Mode 1: D*

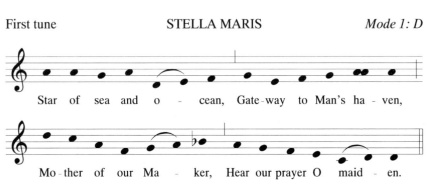

Star of sea and o - cean, Gate-way to Man's ha - ven,
Mo - ther of our Ma - ker, Hear our prayer O maid - en.

Second tune   **AVE MARIS STELLA**

THE BLESSED VIRGIN MARY

305

1. Star of sea and ocean,
   Gateway to Man's[1] haven,
   Mother of our Maker,
   Hear our prayer, O maiden.

2. Welcoming the Ave
   Of God's simple greeting,
   You have borne a Saviour
   Far beyond all dreaming.

3. Loose the bonds that hold us,
   Bound in sin's own blindness,
   That with eyes now opened,
   God's own light may guide us.

4. Show yourself, our Mother:
   He will hear your pleading,
   Whom your womb has sheltered
   And whose hand brings healing.

5. Gentlest of all virgins,
   That our love be faithful,
   Keep us from all evil,
   Gentle, strong and grateful.

6. Guard us through life's dangers,
   Never turn and leave us,
   May our hope find harbour
   In the calm of Jesus.

7. Sing to God our Father
   Through the Son who saves us;
   Joyful in the Spirit
   Everlasting praises.

[1] 'Man' refers generically to the whole human race.

Text: Ralph Wright OSB; from *Ave, maris stella* (8th century). First tune: Alan Rees OSB. Second tune: C. Ett, *Cantica Sacra*, 1840.

306　　　　　　　　　　　　　　　　　　11.11.11.11

First tune　　　　　　　　PARADISO　　　　　　*Mode 1: E*

Bless - ed Vir - gin Mo - ther, daugh - ter of your Son,

High - est of all wo - men, hum - bler there ___ is none.

When you bore the sa - viour by di - vine de - cree,

You gave ___ all cre - a - tion new-found dig - ni - ty.

Second tune　　　　　　　UNE VAINE CRAINTE

THE BLESSED VIRGIN MARY

1   Blessed Virgin Mother, daughter of your Son,
Highest of all women, humbler there is none.
When you bore the saviour by divine decree,
You gave all creation new-found dignity.

2   When the source of hope sprang forth against despair,
And the God of love was nourished by your care,
Then the fire of grace did flourish and increase,
Spreading through the nations news of heavenly peace.

3   You are loving-kindness, ever know our need;
You are all compassion, gladly intercede,
You are all perfection in the human race,
Through your mediation we can share God's grace.

Text: Anthony G. Petti (1932-85); from *Il Paradiso*, Canto 33, Dante Alighieri (1265-1321) First tune: John Harper, based on *Gaudium mundi*. Second tune: melody, French Noël; harmony, John Harper.

Text: © 1971, Faber Music Ltd, 3 Queen Square, London WC1N 3AU; reprinted from *New Catholic Hymnal* by permission of the publishers. First tune and second tune (harmony): © 1995, Panel of Monastic Musicians, Mount Saint Bernard Abbey, Coalville, Leicester LE67 5UL.

307   7.5.7.5

First tune   **PENHALONGA**   *Mode 1: D*

God, who made the earth and sky And the chang - ing sea,

Clothed his glo - ry in our flesh, One with us to be.

Second tune   **SAINT AIDAN**

THE BLESSED VIRGIN MARY

1   God, who made the earth and sky
    And the changing sea,
    Clothed his glory in our flesh,
    One with us to be.

2   Mary, Virgin filled with light,
    Chosen from our race,
    Bore the Father's only Son
    By the Spirit's grace.

3   He whom nothing can contain,
    No one can compel,
    Bound his timeless Godhead here,
    In our time to dwell.

4   God, our Father, Lord of days,
    And his only Son,
    With the Holy Spirit praise:
    Trinity in One.

Text: Stanbrook Abbey; from *Quem terra, pontus*, Venantius Fortunatus? (c. 530-c. 610). First tune: Charles Watson OSB and Peter Allan CR. Second tune: Herbert Popple (1891-1965).

Text: © 1974 and 1995, Stanbrook Abbey, Callow End, Worcester WR2 4TD. First tune: © 1995, Panel of Monastic Musicians, Mount Saint Bernard Abbey, Coalville, Leicester LE67 5UL. Second tune: © Oxford University Press.

308

10.10.10.10

First tune — TERRA PONTUS — *Mode a: A*

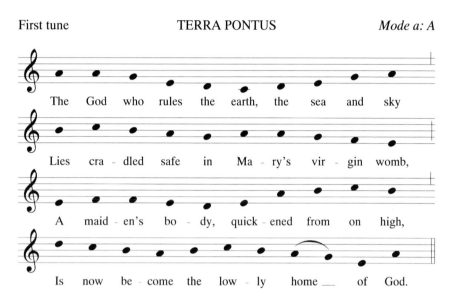

The God who rules the earth, the sea and sky
Lies cra - dled safe in Ma - ry's vir - gin womb,
A maid - en's bo - dy, quick - ened from on high,
Is now be - come the low - ly home — of God.

1   The God who rules the earth, the sea and sky
Lies cradled safe in Mary's virgin womb,
A maiden's body, quickened from on high,
Is now become the lowly home of God.

2   The threefold fabric of this world of time
Adores and praises, cries aloud your name:
Whom sun and moon and all created things
In loving service tirelessly obey.

3   How blest the Mother, whose consent could give
A resting-place of living flesh and blood
To that eternal craftsman who made all,
And in whose hand our world is held secure.

4   The message of the angel brought her joy,
Made fruitful by the Holy Spirit's breath:
The long awaited hope of all the world
Is born of Mary, heir of David's line.

Second tune   FARLEY CASTLE

5   To you, O Lord, the Virgin's only Son,
     We offer praise and glory with our love:
     To Father and the Spirit, bond of love,
     We bow in joy that never has an end.

Text: Mount Saint Bernard Abbey, altered; from *Quem terra, pontus*, Venantius Fortunatus? (c. 530-c. 610). First tune: Alan Rees OSB. Second tune: Henry Lawes (1596-1662).

309 7.5.7.5

First tune CORONA LUCIS *Mode 2: G*

Ma - ry crowned with liv - ing light, Tem - ple of the Lord,

Place of peace and ho - li - ness, Shel - ter of the Word.

Alternative: PENHALONGA, 307

Second tune SAINT AIDAN

THE BLESSED VIRGIN MARY

1   Mary crowned with living light,
    Temple of the Lord,
    Place of peace and holiness,
    Shelter of the Word.

2   Mystery of sinless life
    In our fallen race,
    Free from shadow, you reflect
    Plenitude of grace.

3   Virgin-Mother of our God,
    Lift us when we fall,
    Who were named upon the cross
    Mother of us all.

4   Father, Son and Paraclete,
    Heaven sings your praise,
    Mary magnifies your name
    Through eternal days.

Text: Stanbrook Abbey. First tune: Alan Rees OSB. Second tune: Herbert Popple (1891-1965).

Text: © 1974 and 1995, Stanbrook Abbey, Callow End, Worcester WR2 4TD. First tune: © 1995, Belmont Abbey Trustees, Hereford, HR2 9RZ. Second tune: © Oxford University Press.

310

LM

First tune   **EXULTET CAELUM LAUDIBUS**   *Mode 4: F♯*

Let all ___ on earth ___ their ___ voi - ces raise,

Re - e - cho - ing _____ heaven's tri - um - phant _ praise,

To him who ___ gave ___ the a - post - les grace

To run on ___ earth their _____ glo - rious ___ race.

Second tune   **GONFALON ROYAL**

APOSTLES

1   Let all on earth their voices raise,
Re-echoing heaven's triumphant praise,
To him who gave the apostles grace
To run on earth their glorious race.

2   O servants who once bore the light
Of Gospel truth o'er heathen night,
To us that heavenly light impart,
To glad our eyes and cheer our heart.

3   O Lord, your will to them was given
To bind and loose in earth and heaven,
Our chains unbind, our sins undo,
And in our hearts your grace renew.

4   Strong in your truth, they spoke the word
Which cured disease and health restored,
To us its healing power prolong,
Support the weak, confirm the strong.

5   And when the thrones are set on high
And judgment's awesome hour draws nigh,
Then, Lord, with them pronounce us blest
And take us to your endless rest.

6   Praise we the Father and the Son,
And Holy Spirit, Three in One,
Whom now we worship and adore
For ever and for evermore.

Alternative first tune: IESU, CORONA VIRGINUM, 326

Text: Richard Mant (1775-1848) and others, altered; from *Exultet caelum laudibu*s (10th century?).
Second tune: Percy Buck (1871-1947), harmony adapted.

Text (this version): © 1995, Panel of Monastic Musicians, Mount Saint Bernard Abbey, Coalville, Leicester LE67 5UL. Second tune: © Oxford University Press; adapted by permission.

311

LM

First tune   STRATA FLORIDA   *Mode 1: D*

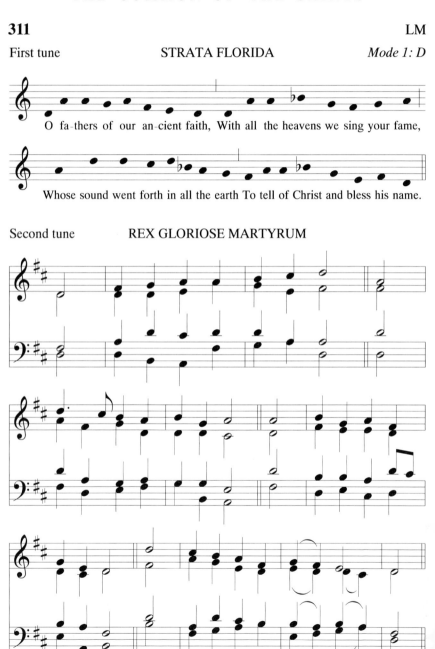

O fa-thers of our an-cient faith, With all the heavens we sing your fame,

Whose sound went forth in all the earth To tell of Christ and bless his name.

Second tune   REX GLORIOSE MARTYRUM

APOSTLES

1   O fathers of our ancient faith,
With all the heavens we sing your fame,
Whose sound went forth in all the earth
To tell of Christ and bless his name.

2   You took the gospel to the poor,
The word of God alight in you,
Which in our day is told again:
That timeless word, forever new.

3   You told of God who died for us
And out of death triumphant rose,
Who gave the truth that made us free,
And changeless through the ages goes.

4   Like sparks among the straw, you ran
To set the universe ablaze,
To kindle love of Christ the Lord
And take his peace on all your ways.

5   Praise Father, Son and Spirit blest
Whose gift is faith that never dies:
A light in darkness now, until
The day star in our hearts arise.

Alternative first tune: EXULTET CAELUM LAUDIBUS, 310

Text: Stanbrook Abbey. First tune: Mount Saint Bernard Abbey. Second tune: adapted from *Katholische Geistliche Gesänge*, Andernach 1608; harmony, probably Ralph Vaughan Williams (1872-1958), altered.

Text: © 1974 and 1995, Stanbrook Abbey, Callow End, Worcester WR2 4TD. First tune: © 1995, Mount Saint Bernard Abbey, Coalville, Leicester LE67 5UL.

312 LM

First tune · O SEMPITERNAE CURIAE · *Mode 3: E*

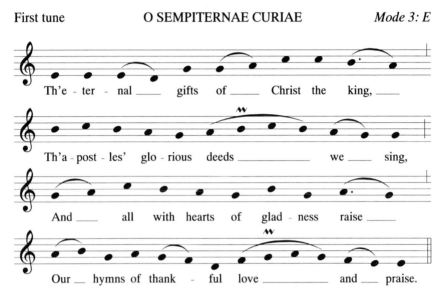

Th'e - ter - nal ___ gifts of ___ Christ the king, ___

Th'a - post - les' glo - rious deeds ___ we ___ sing,

And ___ all with hearts of glad - ness raise ___

Our ___ hymns of thank - ful love ___ and ___ praise.

Alternatives: EXULTET CAELUM LAUDIBUS, 310; FLORES MARTYRUM, 457

1   The eternal gifts of Christ the king,
      The apostles' glorious deeds, we sing,
      And all with hearts of gladness raise
      Our hymns of thankful love and praise.

2   These princes of the Church in light,
      Triumphant leaders in the fight,
      Who stand their guard in heaven above,
      Enlighten us with truth and love.

3   Theirs is the steadfast faith of saints,
      Unconquered hope that never wanes,
      And love of Christ that will not fail,
      But over evil still prevails.

4   In them the Father's glory shone;
      In them rejoices God the Son;
      In them is done the Spirit's will;
      And heaven with praise is ringing still.

Second tune   DEO GRACIAS (AGINCOURT)

5   Redeemer, hear us in your love,
     And bring us with your saints above,
     That we with them may find a place
     Within the kingdom of your grace.

Text: editors' compilation; from *Aeterna Christi munera*, Saint Ambrose (c. 339-397). Second tune: melody, 15th-century English; harmony, John Harper.

313

LM

First tune   IESU, REDEMPTOR SAECULI   *Mode 1: E*

Th'a - post - les' hearts ___ with grief were ___ sore

That they should see ___ their Lord no more,

Whom e - vil minds con - demned to die ___

A death of cru - el a - go - ny.

Second tune   GONFALON ROYAL

APOSTLES IN EASTERTIDE

1   The apostles' hearts with grief were sore
    That they should see their Lord no more,
    Whom evil minds condemned to die
    A death of cruel agony.

2   Then to the women at the grave
    The angel this glad message gave:
    'Fear not, his followers will see
    Their risen Lord in Galilee.'

3   The trusting women went their way,
    Their eager tidings to convey:
    They met the Christ, their living Lord,
    And, falling at his feet, adored.

4   So then the apostles' company
    Set out in haste for Galilee,
    That there once more they might behold
    The Lord's dear face as he foretold.

5   Creator of us all, we pray,
    Fulfil in us your joy today,
    When death assails us, grant that we
    May share your paschal victory.

6   All praise to you, O risen Lord,
    From death to endless life restored;
    All praise to you blest Trinity,
    Both now and in eternity.

Text: John Mason Neale (1818-66) and others, altered; from *Tristes erant apostoli* (10th century?).
Second tune: Percy Buck (1871-1947), harmony adapted.

Text (this version): © 1995, Panel of Monastic Musicians, Mount Saint Bernard Abbey, Coalville,
Leicester LE67 5UL. Second tune: © Oxford University Press; adapted by permission.

314

First tune   AURORA LUCIS RUTILAT (i)   *Mode 8:F*

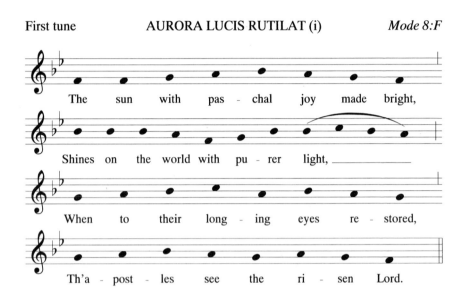

The sun with pas - chal joy made bright,

Shines on the world with pu - rer light, _____

When to their long - ing eyes re - stored,

Th'a - post - les see the ri - sen Lord.

Second tune   O AMOR QUAM EXSTATICUS (RESURREXIT)

APOSTLES IN EASTERTIDE

1   The sun with paschal joy made bright,
        Shines on the world with purer light,
        When to their longing eyes restored,
        The apostles see the risen Lord.

2   He showed the wounds in hands and side,
        Now with his body glorified;
        The signs to all the world made plain,
        That Christ the Lord was risen again.

3   O Jesus, king of gentleness,
        We pray you, Lord, our hearts possess,
        That we may render all our days,
        The willing tribute of our praise.

4   Creator of us all, we pray,
        Fulfil in us your joy today,
        When death assails us, grant that we
        May share your paschal victory.

5   All praise to you, O risen Lord,
        From death to endless life restored;
        All praise to you blest Trinity,
        Both now and in eternity.

Text: John Mason Neale (1818-66), altered; from *Claro paschali gaudio* (11th century). Second tune: French church melody; harmony, Ralph Vaughan Williams (1872-1958), from *The English Hymnal*, altered.

Text (this version): © 1995, Panel of Monastic Musicians, Mount Saint Bernard Abbey, Coalville, Leicester LE67 5UL. Second tune (harmony): © Oxford University Press. Altered by permission.

315

First tune   TE, CATHARINA   *Mode 8: G*

Christ in whose ___ pas - sion once ___ was sown

All vir - tue of ___ the ___ saints ___ to ___ be,

For the white field of these thine own ___

We praise the seed ___ and ___ sow - er, ___ thee.

Alternative: IESU, CORONA VIRGINUM, 326

Second tune   MEIN' SEEL', O GOTT

MARTYRS

1   Christ in whose passion once was sown
     All virtue of the saints to be,
     For the white field of these thine own
     We praise the seed and sower, thee.

2   Thine was the first and holiest grain
     To die and quicken and increase;
     And then came these, for thy sake slain;
     That spring and harvest should not cease.

3   From thee the martyrs, we from those,
     Each in thy grace's measure, spring;
     Their strength upon our weakness flows
     And guides us to the goal we sing.

4   These were thy great ones: we, thy least,
     One in desire and faith with them,
     Called by one Lord to keep one feast,
     Journey to one Jerusalem.

5   To God the Father, harvest's Lord,
     To Christ, for whom the martyrs die;
     To Paraclete, their strength and sword,
     Be praise to all eternity.

Text: Walter H. Shewring, altered Sisters of the Love of God, Fairacres. Second tune: Michael Praetorius (1571-1621).

Text reprinted by permission of Burns and Oates/Search Press Ltd, Wellwood, North Farm Road, Tunbridge Wells, Kent TN2 3DR; alterations © 1981, Sisters of the Love of God, Fairacres Road, Oxford OX4 1TB.

316

LM

First tune · TE, CATHARINA · *Mode 8: G*

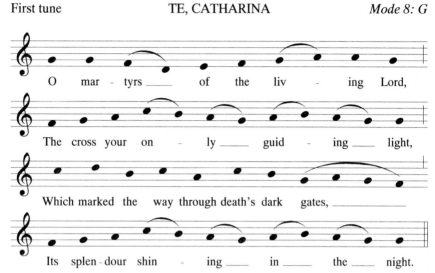

1   O martyrs of the living Lord,
     The cross your only guiding light,
     Which marked the way through death's dark gates,
     Its splendour shining in the night.

2   With Christ you suffered cruel death,
     With Christ you bore defeat and shame;
     With him you share the lasting joys
     He promised in his Father's name.

3   Steadfast and faithful, pray that we
     Who wrestle still to keep his word
     May dare to follow through the dark
     The glorious cross of Christ our Lord.

4   All praise to God the Father be,
     All praise to Christ, his victor-Son,
     All praise to God the Paraclete,
     Most blessed Trinity in One.

MARTYRS

Second tune   REX GLORIOSE MARTYRUM

Alternative first tune: IESU, CORONA VIRGINUM, 326

Text: editors' compilation. Second tune: adapted from *Katholische Geistliche Gesänge*, Andernach 608; harmony, probably Ralph Vaughan Williams (1872-1958), altered.

Text: © 1995, Panel of Monastic Musicians, Mount Saint Bernard Abbey, Coalville, Leicester LE67 UL.

317

First tune   AETERNA CHRISTI MUNERA   *Mode 7: F*

King of the ___ mar-tyrs' no - - ble ___ band,

Crown of the true in _____ ev - 'ry land,

Strength of the pil-grims on ___ their __ way _____

Bea - con by ___ night and cloud _____ by __ day.

Alternative: TE CATHARINA, 315

1   King of the martyrs' noble band,
Crown of the true in every land,
Strength of the pilgrims on their way
Beacon by night and cloud by day.

2   Hear us now as we celebrate
Faith undeterred by ruthless hate;
Hear and forgive us, for we too
Know very well the wrong we do.

3   Dying, through you they overcame;
Living, were faithful to your name.
Turn our rebellious hearts, and thus
Win a like victory in us.

4   Glory to God the Father be,
Glory to Christ who set us free;
And to the Spirit, living flame,
Glory unceasing we proclaim.

MARTYRS

Second tune   DAS NEUGEBORNE KINDELEIN (JENA)

Text: John Webster Grant, altered; from *Rex gloriose martyrum* (6th century). Second tune: melody: Melchior Vulpius (c. 1560-1616); harmony, from J. S. Bach (1685-1750).

Text: © 1971, John Webster Grant, Toronto, Canada.

318

CM

First tune   ABERCONWY   *Mode 2: F♯*

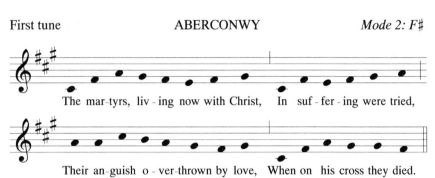

The mar-tyrs, liv - ing now with Christ, In suf - fer - ing were tried,

Their an-guish o - ver-thrown by love, When on his cross they died.

Second tune   SONG 67

MARTYRS

1   The martyrs, living now with Christ,
         In suffering were tried,
         Their anguish overthrown by love,
         When on his cross they died.

2   Across the centuries they come,
         In constancy unmoved,
         Their loving hearts make no complaint;
         In silence they are proved.

3   For who has ever measured love
         Or weighed it in the hand?
         Yet God, who knows the inmost heart,
         Gives them the promised land.

4   Praise Father, Son and Spirit blest,
         Who guide us through the night,
         In ways that reach beyond the stars
         To everlasting light.

Text: Stanbrook Abbey. First tune: Mount Saint Bernard Abbey. Second tune: melody and bass, Orlando Gibbons (1583-1625).

Text: © 1974 and 1995, Stanbrook Abbey, Callow End, Worcester WR2 4TD. First tune: © 1995, Mount Saint Bernard Abbey, Coalville, Leicester LE67 5UL.

319

LM

First tune   AETERNA CHRISTI MUNERA   *Mode 7: F*

Th'e - ter - nal ___ gifts of Christ ___ the ___ king

In all his mar - tyrs' ___ deeds ___ we sing,

With joy - ful heart and voice _ we ___ raise ___

This hymn of ___ thank - ful ___ love and ___ praise.

Second tune   O INVIDENDA MARTYRUM

MARTYRS

1   The eternal gifts of Christ the king
    In all his martyrs' deeds we sing,
    With joyful heart and voice we raise
    This hymn of thankful love and praise.

2   These princes of the Church in light,
    Triumphant leaders in the fight,
    Now watching with the Lord above,
    Inspire us by their faith and love.

3   They suffered long at human hands,
    Their blood was shed in many lands,
    Steadfast till death, they won a place
    Within God's realm of life and grace.

4   In them the Father's glory shone,
    In them rejoices God the Son,
    Through them is done the Spirit's will,
    And heaven with praise is ringing still.

5   O Father, hear our humble prayer,
    That we with all your saints may share
    Such faith in your redeeming might,
    And live for ever in your light.

Alternative first tune: IESU, CORONA VIRGINUM, 326

Text: editors' compilation; from *Aeterna Christi munera et martyrum*. Second tune: melody, Dijon Antiphoner; harmony, Ralph Vaughan Williams (1872-1958), from *The English Hymnal*.

Text: © 1995, Panel of Monastic Musicians, Mount Saint Bernard Abbey, Coalville, Leicester LE67 5UL. Second tune (harmony): © Oxford University Press.

320   8.7.8.7

First tune   **DUX MARTYRUM**   *Mode 2: F♯*

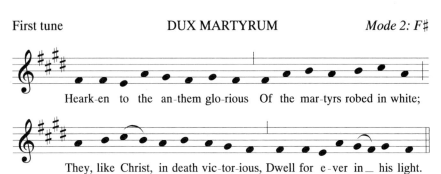

Heark-en to the an-them glo-rious Of the mar-tyrs robed in white;

They, like Christ, in death vic-tor-ious, Dwell for e-ver in — his light.

Second tune   **WYCHBOLD**

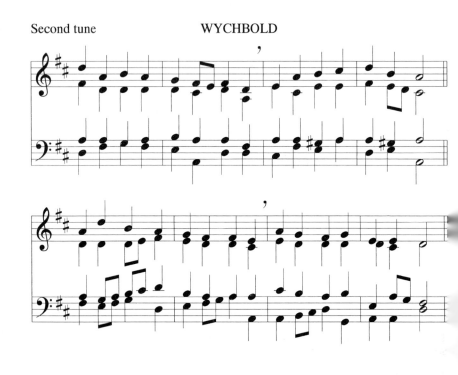

MARTYRS

1   Hearken to the anthem glorious
    Of the martyrs robed in white;
    They, like Christ, in death victorious
    Dwell for ever in his light.

2   Living they proclaimed salvation,
    Filled from heaven with grace and power;
    And they died in imitation
    Of their saviour's final hour.

3   Christ, for cruel traitors pleading,
    Triumphed in his parting breath
    Over all his deeds proceeding
    His inglorious cross-bound death.

4   Take from him what you will give him,
    Of his fulness grace for grace;
    Strive to think him, speak him, live him,
    Till you meet him face to face.

Text: Christopher Smart (1722-71), altered. First tune: editors, adapted from *O qui tuo, dux martyrum*. Second tune: Walter Whinfield (1865-1919).

Text (this version) and first tune: © 1995, Panel of Monastic Musicians, Mount Saint Bernard Abbey, Coalville, Leicester LE67 5UL.

321

LM

First tune · TE, CATHARINA · *Mode 8: G*

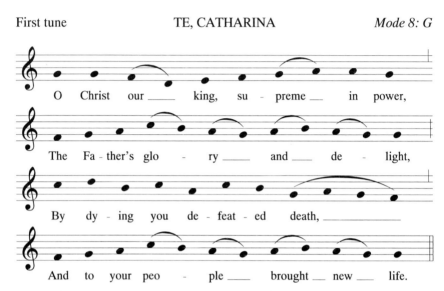

O Christ our —— king, su - preme —— in power,

The Fa - ther's glo - ry —— and —— de - light,

By dy - ing you de - feat - ed death, ——————

And to your peo - ple —— brought —— new —— life.

1   O Christ our king, supreme in power,
       The Father's glory and delight,
       By dying you defeated death,
       And to your people brought new life.

2   In triumph rising from the tomb
       The faithful from the grave you lead;
       Through that great Paschal sacrifice
       From sin and death you set us free.

3   In certain hope of life redeemed
       This martyr to the faith held fast,
       And trusting in the gospel truth
       Did suffer in the name of Christ.

4   Increase in us such hope and trust;
       Lord, bring your Spirit to our aid
       To strengthen and uphold our faith,
       As we your second coming wait.

A MARTYR (MAN OR WOMAN)

321

Second tune   DEUS TUORUM MILITUM

5   Then may we reach the Father's home
           Where all the martyrs and the saints
           Surround the glorious Three in One:
           With them we ever sing your praise.

Text: editors' compilation. Second tune: melody, Grenoble Antiphoner, 1753; harmony, Michael Fleming.

Text: © 1995, Panel of Monastic Musicians, Mount Saint Bernard Abbey, Coalville, Leicester LE67 5UL. Second tune (harmony): © 1986, The Canterbury Press, Norwich NR3 3BH.

322   10.10.10.10

First tune   MARGAM   *Mode 1: D*

We praise those shep-herds of the flock of Christ
Who led it in the ways of truth and right,
In time of e-vil and in dark-est days
Their faith and for-ti-tude a stead-fast light.

1   We praise those shepherds of the flock of Christ
     Who led it in the ways of truth and right,
     In time of evil and in darkest days,
     Their faith and fortitude a steadfast light.

2   God sent his Spirit down upon his priests
     Who offered sacrifice with hallowed hands,
     Who poured out saving water, loosed from sin,
     And took their joyful news to all the lands.

3   They interceded for their people's sins,
     Like Moses, lifting holy hands to pray;
     They are his priests for ever, who received
     The power that none on earth can take away.

4   O blessed Trinity whom we adore,
     The hidden God through our Redeemer known,
     Give constancy and courage to your Church
     Till time into eternity has grown.

Text: Stanbrook Abbey, abbreviated. First tune: Mount Saint Bernard Abbey. Second tune: John Ainslie, harmony adapted.

Text: © 1974, Stanbrook Abbey, Callow End, Worcester WR2 4TD. First tune: © 1995, Mount Saint Bernard Abbey, Coalville, Leicester LE67 5UL. Second tune: © 1972, John Ainslie, Calamus, 30 North Terrace, Mildenhall, Suffolk IP 27 7AB.

EVENING PRAYER

322

Second tune   ELLENBOROUGH

Alternative: MAGDA, 332

323   11.11.11.5

First tune   DOCTOR AETERNUS   *Mode 8: G*

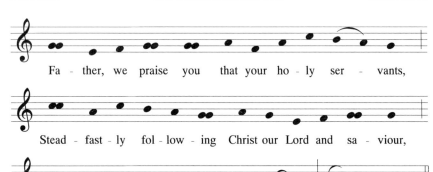

Fa - ther, we praise you that your ho - ly ser - vants,

Stead - fast - ly fol - low - ing Christ our Lord and sa - viour,

Now in your king - dom share with all the faith - ful Vi - sion of glo - ry.

Alternative: NOBILEM CHRISTI, 327

1   Father, we praise you that your holy servants,
     Steadfastly following Christ our Lord and saviour,
     Now in your kingdom share with all the faithful
     Vision of glory.

2   Filled with the Spirit, by their earthly labours,
     Brought to your people healing and compassion;
     Raising the fallen, reconciling sinners,
     Gladly they served them.

3   By their example, prayer and self-denial,
     Preaching and teaching, showing forth the gospel,
     Gave men and women knowledge of your mercy
     And loving-kindness.

4   Joyful thanksgiving now we bring before you,
     Singing with gladness of their life and witness,
     Pledging ourselves to follow in the footsteps
     Of Christ, their master.

5   Glory to you, the Father unbegotten,
     Glory to Christ, the Son of God incarnate,
     And Holy Spirit, fountain of all goodness,
     Trinity blessed.

PASTORS

Second tune CHRISTE SANCTORUM

Text: Sisters of the Love of God, altered. Second tune: melody, Paris Antiphoner, 1681; harmony, Ralph Vaughan Williams (1872-1958), from *The English Hymnal*.

Text: © 1995, Sisters of the Love of God, Fairacres Road, Oxford OX4 1TB. Second tune (harmony): © Oxford University Press.

324

11.11.11.5

First tune

DOCTOR AETERNUS

Mode 8: G

Fa - ther, we praise you that your ho - ly ser - vant,

Stead - fast - ly fol - low - ing Christ our Lord and sa - viour,

Now in your king - dom shares with all the faith - ful Vi - sion of glo - ry.

Alternative: NOBILEM CHRISTI, 327

1   Father, we praise you that your holy servant,
     Steadfastly following Christ our Lord and saviour,
     Now in your kingdom shares with all the faithful
     Vision of glory.

2   Filled with the Spirit, by *his/her* earthly labours,
     Brought to your people healing and compassion;
     Raising the fallen, reconciling sinners,
     Gladly *he/she* served them.

3   By this example, prayer and self-denial,
     Preaching and teaching, showing forth the gospel,
     Gave men and women knowledge of your mercy
     And loving-kindness.

4   Joyful thanksgiving now we bring before you,
     Singing with gladness of *his/her* life and witness,
     Pledging ourselves to follow in the footsteps
     Of Christ, *his/her* master.

5   Glory to you, the Father unbegotten,
     Glory to Christ, the Son of God incarnate,
     And Holy Spirit, fountain of all goodness,
     Trinity blessed.

A PASTOR (MAN OR WOMAN)

Second tune   ISTE CONFESSOR

Text: Sisters of the Love of God, altered. Second tune: melody, Poitiers Antiphoner, 1746.

Text: © 1995, Sisters of the Love of God, Fairacres Road, Oxford OX4 1TB.

325　　　　　　　　　　　　　　　　　　　　　11.11.11.5

First tune　　　　　　　DOCTOR AETERNUS　　　　　　*Mode 8: G*

Je - su, our mas - ter and our on - ly sa - viour,

In a - do - ra - tion we ac - claim your teach - ing,

You a-lone of - fer _ words of life e-ter - nal, Laws of sal-va-tion.

Alternative: NOBILEM CHRISTI, 327

1　Jesus, our master and our only saviour,
　In adoration we acclaim your teaching,
　You alone offer words of life eternal,
　Laws of salvation.

2　Humbly we thank you, shepherd through the ages,
　For the protection to your Church extended,
　Constantly guiding, that all souls may find there
　Light in the darkness.

3　Wisest of scholars were your eager servants,
　Stars of great splendour with but one intention,
　Deeper to ponder teachings that might show us
　Life ever blessed.

4　All tongues should praise you, Jesus, Lord and master,
　Who showers treasures through your Holy Spirit,
　By words and writings of the Church's doctors,
　Flame ever fruitful.

5　May this day's patron whom we gladly honour,
　Ever be near us, leading on your people,
　Till we all praise you, faith and hope rewarded,
　In love eternal.

Second tune   ISTE CONFESSOR

Text: Saint Cecilia's Abbey, Ryde, altered; from *Doctor aeternus* (20th century). Second tune: melody, Poitiers Antiphoner, 1746.

Text: © 1976, Benedictine nuns of Saint Cecilia's Abbey, Ryde, Isle of Wight PO33 1LH.

326   LM

First tune   IESU, CORONA VIRGINUM   *Mode 8: G*

Lord Je - sus Christ, the vir-gin's crown, Now gra-cious-ly to us bow down,

Born of that Vir-gin who a-lone God - bear - ing Mo - ther true we own.

1 Lord Jesus Christ, the virgins' crown,
   Now graciously to us bow down,
   Born of that Virgin who alone
   God-bearing Mother true we own.

2 In you, their bridegroom and true Lord,
   The virgins find their bright reward;
   They follow where you lead and sing:
   Glad hymns of praise around you ring.

3 O gracious Lord, to you we pray,
   Pour out on us your grace today;
   Keep us in faith both pure and true,
   From sinful darkness free for you.

4 Lord Jesus, virgin-born, we raise
   To you our hymn of thankful praise;
   To God the holy Trinity
   Be glory in eternity.

Second tune   IESU, CORONA VIRGINUM

Text: John Mason Neale (1818-66) and others, altered; from *Iesu, corona virginum*, Saint Ambrose? (c. 339-397). Second tune: melody, Rouen Antiphoner, 1728; harmony, Ralph Vaughan Williams (1872-1958), from *The English Hymnal*, altered.

Text (this version): © 1995, Panel of Monastic Musicians, Mount Saint Bernard Abbey, Coalville, Leicester LE67 5UL. Second tune (harmony): © Oxford University Press. Altered by permission.

327   11.11.11.5

First tune   NOBILEM CHRISTI   *Mode 2: F♯*

Son of a vir-gin, ma-ker of your mo-ther:

Vir-gin con-ceiv-ing, vir-gin still re-main-ing:

Lord, on this feast-day of a saint-ly vir-gin, Hear our pe-ti-tion.

1   Son of a virgin, maker of your mother:
       Virgin conceiving, virgin still remaining:
       Lord, on this feastday of a saintly virgin,
       Hear our petition.

2   She, in her virtue, gained a double blessing,
       Who, in her body vanquishing the weakness,
       In that same body, grace from heaven obtaining,
       Bore the world witness.

3   Death, nor the rending pains of death appalled her,
       Anguish and torment found her undefeated:
       So by the shedding of her life attained she
       Riches in heaven.

4   Fountain of mercy, hear the prayers she offers;
       Purge our offences, pardon our transgressions;
       Thus with a pure heart we may come before you
       Singing your praises.

5   Almighty Father, with the Son incarnate
       And Holy Spirit, Three in One co-equal,
       Glory be henceforth yours through all the ages,
       Word without ending.

A VIRGIN

327

Second tune   DIVA SERVATRIX

Text: Laurence Housman (1865-1959), from *The English Hymnal*, altered; from *Virginis proles* (9th century). Second tune: Bayeux Antiphoner, 1739; harmony, Ralph Vaughan Williams (1872-1958), from *The English Hymnal*, altered.

Text and second tune (harmony): © Oxford University Press.

328

LM

First tune   IESU, CORONA VIRGINUM   *Mode 8: G*

The call _ to ho - li-ness is ours, As to the saints whom we _ re-vere;

The Spi-rit of the Lord still speaks In our_ own hearts, if we will hear.

Second tune   SOLEMNIS HAEC FESTIVITAS

HOLY MEN AND WOMEN

1   The call to holiness is ours,
     As to the saints whom we revere;
     The Spirit of the Lord still speaks
     In our own hearts, if we will hear.

2   The Father's love is never spent:
     His promise firm, his mercy sure.
     He gives his Son to be our way,
     Our truth, our life, and rock secure.

3   Within the vine all branches bear
     New fruits of love, rich wine outpoured
     In joyful service, toil and prayer
     Made holy by the holy Lord.

4   By serving all, they serve their king;
     By praising him, to all belong;
     The saints with us God's glory sing,
     And Alleluia is their song.

Text: Wetherby Carmel. Second tune: melody, Paris Gradual, 1685; harmony, John Harper.

Text: © 1995 The Carmelite Monastery, Wood Hall, Linton, Wetherby, West Yorkshire LS22 4HZ. Second tune (harmony): © 1995, Panel of Monastic Musicians, Mount Saint Bernard Abbey, Coalville, Leicester LE67 5UL.

329

LM

First tune   NETLEY   *Mode 3: E*

Lord Je - sus, when you dwelt on earth And healed the wounds of sin and death,

Your words made known with gen-tle power The mys-t'ry of the Fa-ther's love.

Alternative: IESU, CORONA CELSIOR, 330

Second tune   DEUS TUORUM MILITUM

HOLY MEN AND WOMEN

1 Lord Jesus, when you dwelt on earth
   And healed the wounds of sin and death,
   Your words made known with gentle power
   The mystery of the Father's love.

2 You are yourself the way to God,
   His saving truth that makes us free,
   The life of everlasting peace,
   Abiding joy of all your saints.

3 We thank you for your Spirit-gift,
   We praise you for his gracious love,
   Restoring with unfailing care
   Your likeness in our human hearts.

4 Eternal Father, God of peace,
   May you be blest in all your saints,
   With Jesus, your beloved Son
   And with the Spirit Paraclete.

Text: Mount Saint Bernard Abbey, altered. First tune: Mount Saint Bernard Abbey. Second tune: melody, Grenoble Antiphoner, 1753; harmony, Michael Fleming.

Text and first tune: © 1995, Mount Saint Bernard Abbey, Coalville, Leicester LE67 5UL. Second tune (harmony): © 1986, The Canterbury Press, Norwich NR3 3BH.

330

First tune   IESU, CORONA CELSIOR   *Mode 8: G*

O Je-sus, sa-viour of us _ all, From whom the saints re-ceived their call,

On this com-me-mo-ra-tion day ____ Hear, Lord, your peo-ple as they pray.

Second tune   O INVIDENDA MARTYRUM

Alternative: DEUS TUORUM MILITUM, 329

HOLY MEN

1   O Jesus, saviour of us all,
From whom the saints received their call,
On this commemoration day
Hear, Lord, your people as they pray.

2   Contending for your holy name,
Your servants won their saintly fame,
Which Christian hearts with praise recall,
And bless the Lord and God of all.

3   Earth's fleeting pleasures counting nought,
For higher, truer joys they sought,
And now with angels round your throne,
Unfading glories are their own.

4   O grant that we, most gracious God,
May follow in the steps they trod,
And freed from every bond of sin,
As they have won, may also win.

5   To you, O Christ, most loving king,
All glory, praise and thanks we bring,
Whom with the Father we adore,
And Holy Spirit, evermore.

Text: Father Benson SSJE (1824-1915), altered; from *Iesu, redemptor omnium* (8th century). Second tune: melody, Dijon Antiphoner; harmony, Ralph Vaughan Williams (1872-1958), from *The English Hymnal*.

Text (this version): © 1995, Panel of Monastic Musicians, Mount Saint Bernard Abbey, Coalville, Leicester LE67 5UL. Second tune (harmony): © Oxford University Press. Altered by permission.

331   SM

First tune   MIRFIELD   *Mode 1: D*

Blest are the pure in heart, For they shall see our God,

The se - cret of the Lord is theirs, Their soul is Christ's a - bode.

Second tune   FRANCONIA

HOLY MEN

1   Blest are the pure in heart,
For they shall see our God,
The secret of the Lord is theirs,
Their soul is Christ's abode.

2   The Lord who left the heavens
Our life and peace to bring,
To dwell in lowliness on earth,
Our pattern and our king.

3   Still to the lowly soul
He doth himself impart
And for his dwelling and his throne
Chooseth the pure in heart.

4   Lord we thy presence seek;
May ours this blessing be;
Give us a pure and lowly heart,
A temple meet for thee.

Text: John Keble (1792-1866) and William John Hall (1793-1861), altered. First tune: Charles Watson OSB and Peter Allan CR. Second tune: melody adapted from König, *Harmonischer Lieder-Schatz*, Frankfurt 1738 by William Havergal (1793-1870).

First tune: © 1995, Panel of Monastic Musicians, Mount Saint Bernard Abbey, Coalville, Leicester LE67 5UL.

332   10.10.10.10

First tune   MARGAM   *Mode 1: D*

Lord Je - sus, joy and crown of all your saints,

Ac - cept the hymn of praise we sing this day,

In glad re - mem - brance of these ho - ly men,

Who sought to fol - low you in faith and love.

1   Lord Jesus, joy and crown of all your saints,
        Accept the hymn of praise we sing this day,
        In glad remembrance of these holy men,
        Who sought to follow you in faith and love.

2   In darkness and temptation purified,
        With persevering hope, unfailing trust,
        Sustained by grace, they chose the path you trod,
        Embraced the cross made holy by your blood.

3   Raised up to glory, honoured by your Church,
        They share the joy you promised to your friends,
        With you and all your saints they lift their voice
        To plead our cause before your Father's throne.

4   We bless your holy name, Lord Jesus Christ;
        Your Father's glory ever on our lips.
        Your Spirit, too, whose peace has filled our hearts,
        Be praised, adored and loved for evermore.

Text: Mount Saint Bernard Abbey, altered. First tune: Mount Saint Bernard Abbey. Second tune: Ralp
Vaughan Williams (1872-1958), from *Enlarged Songs of Praise 1931*.

Text and first tune: © 1995, Mount Saint Bernard Abbey, Coalville, Leicester LE67 5UL. Second tune
© Oxford University Press.

HOLY MEN

Second tune   MAGDA

Alternative: ELLENBOROUGH, 322

333   11.11.11.5

First tune   CRASSWALL   *Mode 2: F♯*

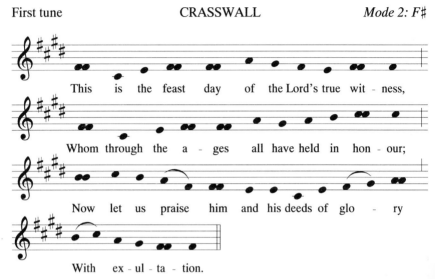

This is the feast day of the Lord's true wit - ness,

Whom through the a - ges all have held in hon - our;

Now let us praise him and his deeds of glo - ry

With ex - ul - ta - tion.

1   This is the feast day of the Lord's true witness,
     Whom through the ages all have held in honour;
     Now let us praise him and his deeds of glory
     With exultation.

2   So now together, giving God the glory,
     We sing his praises and his mighty triumph,
     That in his glory we may all be sharers,
     Now and hereafter.

3   Praise to the Father and the Son most holy,
     Praise to the Spirit, godhead co-eternal,
     Who give examples in the lives of all saints,
     That we may follow.

A HOLY MAN

Second tune   ISTE CONFESSOR

Text: editors' compilation; from *Iste confessor* (8th century). First tune: Alan Rees OSB. Second tune: Poitiers Antiphoner, 1746.

Text: © 1995, Panel of Monastic Musicians, Mount Saint Bernard Abbey, Coalville, Leicester LE67 UL. First tune: © 1995, Belmont Abbey Trustees, Hereford, HR2 9RZ.

334

11.11.11.5

First tune   CRASSWALL   *Mode 2: F♯*

This, Christ's true ser - vant, whol - ly to him gi - ven,

Whom all the faith - ful now re - joice to ho - nour,

On this his feast _ day is with high - est prai - ses

Greet - ed in hea - ven.

1   This, Christ's true servant, wholly to him given,
      Whom all the faithful now rejoice to honour,
      On this his feast day is with highest praises
      Greeted in heaven.

2   Filled with all virtues, pure of heart and humble,
      Prudent and steadfast, loving God in all things,
      Led by the Spirit, he obeyed his master
      While in this body.

3   Surely in answer to his prayers for sinners,
      Christ our redeemer will, with deep compassion,
      Look on our weakness, raise us up and heal us,
      Giving his blessing.

4   So now together, singing his honour,
      Gladly we praise him, and his intercession
      With God our Father, that he may forgive us
      All our offences.

5   Source of salvation, Lord of endless beauty,
      Ruler of all things, saviour of your people,
      To you be glory, reigning in your heaven,
      God in Three Persons.

A HOLY MAN

Second tune   ISTE CONFESSOR

Text: unascribed. First tune: Alan Rees OSB. Second tune: Poitiers Antiphoner, 1746.

First tune: © 1995, Belmont Abbey Trustees, Hereford, HR2 9RZ.

389

335   10.10.10.10

First tune   MARGAM   *Mode 1: D*

Lord Jesus, joy and crown of all your saints,
Accept the hymn of praise we sing this day,
In glad remembrance of this holy man,
Who sought to follow you in faith and love.

1   Lord Jesus, joy and crown of all your saints,
     Accept the hymn of praise we sing this day,
     In glad remembrance of this holy man,
     Who sought to follow you in faith and love.

2   In darkness and temptation purified,
     With persevering hope, unfailing trust,
     Sustained by grace, he chose the path you trod,
     Embraced the cross made holy by your blood.

3   Raised up to glory, honoured by your Church,
     He shares the joy you promised to your friends,
     With you and all your saints he lifts his voice
     To plead our cause before your Father's throne.

4   We bless your holy name, Lord Jesus Christ;
     Your Father's glory ever on our lips.
     Your Spirit, too, whose peace has filled our hearts,
     Be praised, adored and loved for evermore.

A HOLY MAN

Second tune   MAGDA

336

LM

First tune   IESU, CORONA VIRGINUM   *Mode 8: G*

Now let＿ us all＿ our voi-ces raise   To sing that ho -ly wo - man's praise,

Whose name with heav'n -ly glo - ry bright Shines in＿th'e-ter - nal realms of light.

1   Now let us all our voices raise
       To sing that holy woman's praise,
       Whose name with heavenly glory bright
       Shines in the eternal realms of light.

2   Through suffering by the Spirit led,
       With prayer her hungering soul she fed,
       And, strong in faith and patience, trod
       The narrow path that leads to God.

3   O Christ, the strength of all the strong,
       To whom alone high deeds belong,
       Like her, may we attend your call
       To serve and love you best of all.

4   To you, Lord Jesus, glory be,
       In whom we hope eternally,
       That we may gain our true reward,
       And be forever with the Lord.

A HOLY WOMAN

Second tune   IESU, CORONA VIRGINUM

Text: editors' compilation; from *Fortem virili pectore*, Silvius Antoniano (d. 1608). Second tune: melody, Rouen Antiphoner, 1728; harmony, Ralph Vaughan Williams (1872-1958), from *The English Hymnal*, altered.

Text: © 1995, Panel of Monastic Musicians, Mount Saint Bernard Abbey, Coalville, Leicester LE67 5UL. Second tune (harmony): © Oxford University Press. Altered by permission.

337

6.5.5.5

STOCKS BANK

Mode 1: D

A God - fear - ing wo - man Most wor - thy of praise,

Kept faith with the Lord Through all ____ her life's ways.

A HOLY WOMAN

1   A God-fearing woman
       Most worthy of praise,
       Kept faith with the Lord
       Through all her life's ways.

2   Her hands swift to service,
       Her words true and wise;
       God's peace in her heart,
       God's love in her eyes.

3   Through labours and trials
       Adoring him still,
       She mirrored the light
       Of God's holy will.

4   All praise to the Father,
       All praise to the Son,
       All praise to their Spirit,
       Our God, Three in One.

Text: Golders Green Carmel, altered. Tune: Charles Watson OSB and Peter Allan CR.

Text: © 1995, Carmel, Bridge Lane, Golders Green, London NW11 9JT. Tune: © 1995, Panel of Monastic Musicians, Mount Saint Bernard Abbey, Coalville, Leicester LE67 5UL.

338

11.11.11.5

First tune   CRASSWALL   *Mode 2: F♯*

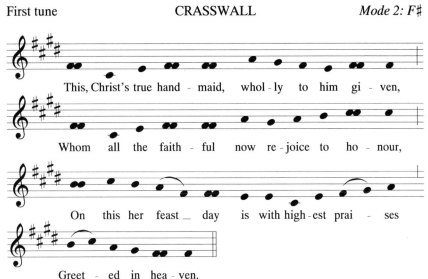

This, Christ's true hand-maid, whol-ly to him gi-ven,

Whom all the faith-ful now re-joice to ho-nour,

On this her feast _ day is with high-est prai - ses

Greet - ed in hea - ven.

1   This, Christ's true handmaid, wholly to him given,
        Whom all the faithful now rejoice to honour,
        On this her feast day is with highest praises
        Greeted in heaven.

2   Filled with all virtues, pure of heart and humble,
        Prudent and steadfast, loving God in all things,
        Led by the Spirit, she obeyed her master
        While in this body.

3   Surely in answer to her prayers for sinners,
        Christ our redeemer will with deep compassion
        Look on our weakness, raise us up and heal us,
        Giving his blessing.

4   So now together, singing her honour,
        Gladly we praise her, and her intercession
        With God our Father, that he may forgive us
        All our offences.

A HOLY WOMAN

338

Second tune   DIVA SERVATRIX

5   Source of salvation, Lord of endless beauty,
        Ruler of all things, saviour of your people,
        To you be glory, reigning in your heaven,
        God in Three Persons.

Text: unascribed. First tune: Alan Rees OSB. Second tune: Bayeux Antiphoner, 1739; harmony, Ralph Vaughan Williams (1872-1958), from *The English Hymnal*, altered.

First tune: © 1995, Belmont Abbey Trustees, Hereford, HR2 9RZ. Second tune (harmony): © Oxford University Press. Altered by permission.

339

8.7.8.7.8.7

First tune   GALLI CANTU   *Mode 2: G*

Sons and daugh-ters of the cloi-ster, Scho-lars of the mas - ter's school;

Work-ers in his work-shop, tak-ing   To each task its fit - ting _ tool;

Prompt-ly you o-beyed his bid-ding Guid-ed by his ho - ly rule.

1   Sons and daughters of the cloister,
      Scholars of the master's school;
      Workers in his workshop, taking
      To each task its fitting tool;
      Promptly you obeyed his bidding
      Guided by his holy rule.

2   You withdrew into the desert
      Seeking there the Lord you chose;
      Through its wastes, though parched and arid,
      Yet his living water flows;
      So the desert at your labours
      Blossomed as the fragrant rose.

3   Ever holding nothing dearer
      Than the love of Christ your Lord,
      You rejoiced to sing his praises
      Mind and voice in one accord;
      Saw and served him in your neighbour
      And his presence there adored.

4   Now it falls for us to follow,
      Making Christ our only care;
      Guided by your life's example,
      Aided by your constant prayer;
      Till we join your choir in heaven
      And with you adore him there.

Second tune   NASHDOM

Alternative first tunes: URBS IERUSALEM BEATA, 304; CYMER, 340

Alternative second tune: SAINT THOMAS, 340

Text: Augustine Morris OSB, altered. Second tune: Anthony Greening.

Text and second tune: © 1995, Elmore Abbey, Church Lane, Speen, Newbury, Berkshire RG13 1SA, by permission of the abbot and community.

340
First tune CYMER
8.7.8.7.8.7
Mode 2: G

Long a-go you _ called your peo-ple, Led them out of _ E-gypt's yoke,

Brought them to your ho-ly moun-tain, Where you spoke in fire and storm:

Mo-ses was the man of vi - sion, He a-lone might see and _ live.

1   Long ago you called your people,
        Led them out of Egypt's yoke,
        Brought them to your holy mountain,
        Where you spoke in fire and storm:
        Moses was the man of vision,
        He alone might see and live.

2   Christ is God, was seen and handled,
        Lived and suffered as a man,
        Died and rose for our salvation,
        Breathes his spirit on us still.
        Yet the vision fades too quickly:
        Every age must see it fresh.

3   Saintly men and holy women
        Glimpsed this vision from afar,
        Strove to leave all else behind them,
        Faithful to their Master's call.
        Once again the desert blossomed,
        Echoed with their songs of praise.

4   Father, grant that we, their children,
        May like them be true in prayer,
        Lovers of this house and Order,
        Jesus Christ our living Rule;
        Finding yet again the desert,
        Where our hearts may hear your voice.

Second tune   SAINT THOMAS

5   Glory be to God the Father,
       Calling us with tireless love.
       Glory be to Christ our Saviour,
       Living with us all our days.
       Glory to their living Spirit,
       Gift of love, of life and hope.

Alternative first tunes: URBS IERUSALEM BEATA, 304; GALLI CANTU, 339
Alternative second tune: NASHDOM, 339

Text: Mount Saint Bernard Abbey, altered. First tune: Mount Saint Bernard Abbey. Second tune: Samuel
Webbe, *Motetts or Antiphons*, 1792.
Text and first tune: © 1995, Mount Saint Bernard Abbey, Coalville, Leicester LE67 5UL.

341   10.10.10.10

First tune   BYLAND   *Mode 2: G*

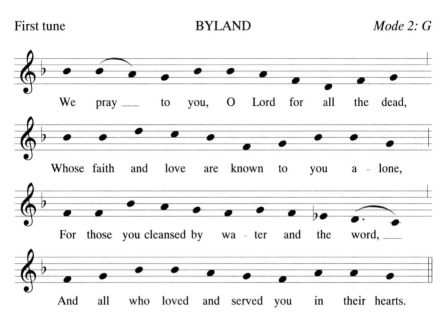

We pray to you, O Lord for all the dead,
Whose faith and love are known to you a-lone,
For those you cleansed by wa-ter and the word,
And all who loved and served you in their hearts.

1   We pray to you, O Lord, for all the dead,
     Whose faith and love are known to you alone,
     For those you cleansed by water and the word,
     And all who loved and served you in their hearts.

2   They know at last the God for whom they sought,
     Have mercy on their weakness and their sins:
     The wounds of Christ have tongues to plead their cause:
     He rose from death that they might live with him.

3   We bow in prayer and praise to you our God,
     And to your Christ, whose death has brought us life,
     Whose Spirit, as a pledge of life to come,
     Still broods above the chaos of our world.

THE DEAD

Second tune   SURSUM CORDA

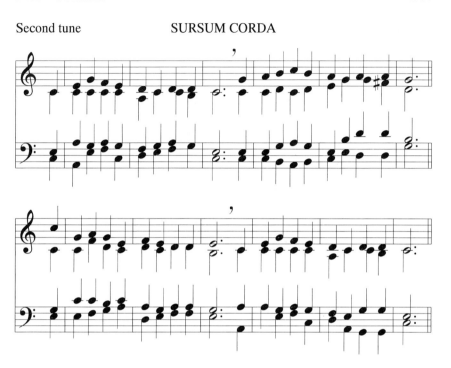

Text: Mount Saint Bernard Abbey, altered. First tune: Mount Saint Bernard Abbey. Second tune: Alfred
M. Smith (1879-1971), harmony adapted.

Text and first tune: © 1995, Mount Saint Bernard Abbey, Coalville, Leicester LE67 5UL. Second tune:
℗ executors of Alfred Morton Smith.

First tune   IUDICA ME   *Mode 1: D*

Word of God, from Ma - ry's _ womb, Born to die for our sal - va - tion,

Laid to rest with-in the _ tomb, Ri - sen Lord of all cre - a - tion:

Bread of life with new life feed _ us, Bread of heaven, to hea - ven lead _ us.

1   Word of God, from Mary's womb,
     Born to die for our salvation,
     Laid to rest within the tomb,
     Risen Lord of all creation:
     Bread of life, with new life feed us,
     Bread from heaven, to heaven lead us.

2   Shepherd-king, for us you bled,
     Guard your sheep in love's safe keeping;
     Welcome home your faithful dead,
     Where no sound is heard of weeping:
     Loving shepherd, walk beside them,
     Through death's darkness safely guide them.

3   Living Lord, you conquered death,
     Come and take away our sadness;
     Breathe on us the Spirit's breath,
     Give us hope of heaven's gladness:
     Word of peace, all sorrow healing,
     Speak, your Father's love revealing.

THE DEAD

Second tune　　　　　　LIEBSTER JESU

Text: James Quinn SJ. First tune: Cecilia Cavenaugh OC. Second tune: melody adapted from Johann Rudolph Ahle (1625-73).

Text: © 1969, James Quinn SJ and Geoffrey Chapman, a Cassell imprint, Wellington House, Strand, London WC2R 0BB. First tune: © 1995, Saint Bernard's Convent, Slough, Berkshire SL3 7AF.

343

CM

First tune · MIRFIELD · *Mode 1: D*

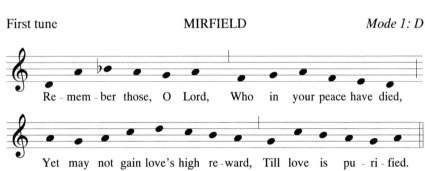

Re - mem - ber those, O Lord, Who in your peace have died,

Yet may not gain love's high re - ward, Till love is pu - ri - fied.

Second tune · FRANCONIA

THE DEAD

1   Remember those, O Lord,
      Who in your peace have died,
      Yet may not gain love's high reward
      Till love is purified.

2   With you they faced death's night,
      Sealed with your victory sign,
      Soon may the splendour of your light
      On them for ever shine.

3   Sweet is their pain, yet deep,
      Till perfect love is born;
      Their lone night-watch they gladly keep
      Before your radiant morn.

4   Your love is their great joy,
      Your will their one desire;
      As finest gold without alloy
      Refine them in love's fire.

5   For them we humbly pray,
      Perfect them in your love;
      O may we share eternal day
      With them in heaven above.

Text: James Quinn SJ. First tune: Charles Watson OSB and Peter Allan CR. Second tune: melody adapted from *König, Harmonischer Lieder-Schatz,* Frankfurt 1738 by William Havergal (1793-1870).

Ω

THE PROPER
OF THE SAINTS

401-457

401   LM

First tune   AURORA LUCIS RUTILAT (ii)   *Mode 7: E*

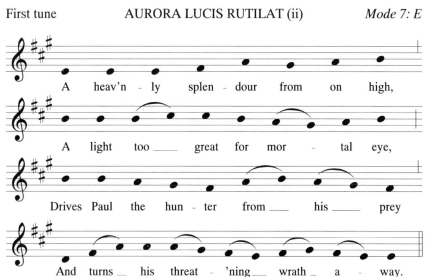

A heav'n - ly splen - dour from on high,

A light too ___ great for mor - tal eye,

Drives Paul the hun - ter from ___ his ___ prey

And turns ___ his threat - 'ning ___ wrath ___ a - way.

1   A heavenly splendour from on high,
      A light too great for mortal eye,
      Drives Paul the hunter from his prey
      And turns his threatening wrath away.

2   In darkened eyes, an inward light
      Begins to shine upon his sight,
      As in his heart he hears the call
      To follow, and surrender all.

3   The Christ, for sinners crucified,
      Whose risen power he had denied,
      Now claims this servant for his own,
      And bids him make the gospel known.

4   The nations listen to his voice,
      And in the peace of Christ rejoice;
      The Church on earth his praises sing,
      Who led the gentiles to their king.

5   To God the Father, God the Son,
      And God the Spirit, Three in One,
      From saints on earth and saints in heaven,
      Let everlasting praise be given.

410

Second tune   REX GLORIOSE MARTYRUM

Text: G. B. Timms, abbreviated and altered. Second tune: Second tune: adapted from *Katholische Geistliche Gesänge*, Andernach 1608; harmony, probably Ralph Vaughan Williams (1872-1958), altered.

Text: © 1986, The Canterbury Press, Norwich NR3 3BH.

411

402

First tune   O SEMPITERNAE CURIAE   *Mode 3: E*

From hea - ven's __ height Christ __ spoke to call __

The gen - tiles' great a - post - - - le, __ Paul,

Whose __ teach - ing like the thun - der sounds __

Through all the world's re - mo - - test __ bounds.

Second tune   SOLEMNIS HAEC FESTIVITAS

THE CONVERSION OF SAINT PAUL

1   From heaven's height Christ spoke to call
    The gentiles' great apostle, Paul,
    Whose teaching like the thunder sounds
    Through all the world's remotest bounds.

2   The Word's good seed to all he brings,
    From which abundant harvest springs;
    And fruits of holy works supply
    God's everlasting granary.

3   The lamp his burning faith displays
    Has filled the world with glorious rays.
    That evil may be overthrown,
    May Christ reign in our hearts alone.

4   To God the Father, God the Son,
    And God the Spirit, Three in One,
    From saints on earth and saints in heaven,
    Let everlasting praise be given.

Text: vv 1-3, John Mason Neale (1818-66) and others, altered; v 4, G. B. Timms; from *Excelsam Pauli gloriam*, Saint Peter Damian (1007-72). Second tune: melody, Paris Gradual, 1685; harmony, John Harper.

403

First tune · ABERCONWY · *Mode 2: F♯*

O gent-ly blind-ing glo-rious light, We praise you for that day

On which the man from Tar - sus found New eyes to see your way.

Second tune · SONG 67

THE CONVERSION OF SAINT PAUL

1   O gently blinding glorious light,
    We praise you for that day
    On which the man from Tarsus found
    New eyes to see your way.

2   For Jesus met him on the road
    And called him by his name;
    And Saul through blindness found the light
    That now he would proclaim.

3   That light reveals a greater world,
    The world of Christ your Son;
    It is a fire within the heart
    That longs for him to come.

4   It is the Spirit of your Son,
    A vision for our eyes;
    The life of God is shared with us
    And all who are baptised.

5   We thank you for the Spirit's light
    Revealed to Paul this day;
    We thank you, Father, for your Son,
    Our light, our truth, our way.

Text: Ralph Wright OSB. First tune: Mount Saint Bernard Abbey. Second tune: melody and bass, Orlando Gibbons (1583-1625).

404   11.11.11.5

First tune   QUOD CHORUS VATUM   *Mode 8: G*

Sing how the age - long pro-mise of a Sa - viour

Fore - told by pro - phets speak-ing in the Spi - rit,

In bless - ed Ma - ry, Mo - ther of the Christ - child,

Finds its ful - fil - ment.

1   Sing how the age-long promise of a Saviour
    Foretold by prophets speaking in the Spirit,
    In blessed Mary, mother of the Christ-child,
    Finds its fulfilment.

2   Purest of virgins, wondrously conceiving,
    In awed obedience, bearing God incarnate,
    Now she presents him for a spotless offering
    Unto his Father.

3   In God's high temple, Simeon the righteous
    With holy rapture, in his arms receives him;
    Joyful his greeting for the one awaited,
    Jesus, Messiah.

4   Where now his mother with her Son is seated,
    In those fair mansions of the heavenly kingdom;
    May Christ our saviour grant to us his servants
    Life everlasting.

5   Father eternal, Son, and Holy Spirit,
    Trinity blessed, maker and redeemer,
    Giver of all life, author of salvation,
    Yours be the glory.

Second tune   DIVA SERVATRIX

Text: *The New English Hymnal*, altered; from *Quod chorus vatum*, Rabanus Maurus (776/84-856).
Second tune: Bayeux Antiphoner, 1739; harmony, Ralph Vaughan Williams (1872-1958), from *The English Hymnal*, altered.

405

10.9.10.9

First tune   PADDINGTON   *Mode 1: D*

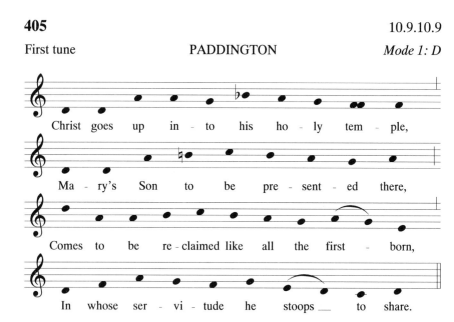

Christ goes up in - to his ho - ly tem - ple,

Ma - ry's Son to be pre - sent - ed there,

Comes to be re - claimed like all the first - born,

In whose ser - vi - tude he stoops _ to share.

Second tune   LLANGOED

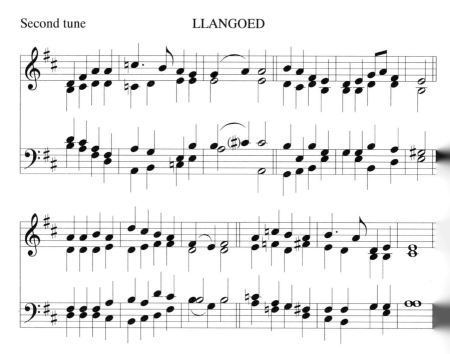

THE PRESENTATION OF CHRIST

1   Christ goes up into his holy temple,
      Mary's Son to be presented there,
      Comes to be reclaimed like all the first-born,
      In whose servitude he stoops to share.

2   Christ was consecrated by his Father,
      Signed with death before his human birth;
      Now the Lord is offered by his mother,
      Sacrificial lamb of precious worth.

3   God, the loving Father of all nations,
      With his Son and Holy Spirit praise;
      Through the ages, Israel's great glory
      Lights the gentile on the Lord's new ways.

Text: Stanbrook Abbey. First tune: Alan Rees OSB. Second tune: John Harper.

Text: © 1974 and 1995, Stanbrook Abbey, Callow End, Worcester WR2 4TD. First tune: © 1995, Belmont Abbey Trustees, Hereford, HR2 9RZ. Second tune: © 1995, Panel of Monastic Musicians, Mount Saint Bernard Abbey, Coalville, Leicester LE67 5UL.

406   6.6.6.6

First tune   BETHANIA   *Mode 8: E*

Hail to ____ the Lord who comes, Comes to his tem - ple gate,

Not with his an - gel hosts,   Not in his king - ly state;

Second tune   SAINT CECILIA

THE PRESENTATION OF CHRIST

1   Hail to the Lord who comes,
    Comes to his temple gate,
    Not with his angel hosts,
    Not in his kingly state;

2   But borne upon the throne
    Of Mary's gentle breast;
    Thus to his Father's house
    He comes, a humble guest.

1   The world's true light draws near
    All darkness to dispel;
    The flame of faith is lit
    And dies the power of hell.

4   Our bodies and our souls
    Are temples now for him,
    For we are born of grace;
    God lights our souls within.

5   O light of all the earth,
    One glorious Trinity;
    The chains of darkness gone
    God's people are set free.

Text: John Ellerton (1826-93), altered. First tune: Alan Rees OSB. Second tune: L. G. Hayne (1836-83).

Text (this version): © 1995, Panel of Monastic Musicians, Mount Saint Bernard Abbey, Coalville, Leicester LE67 5UL. First tune: © 1995, Belmont Abbey Trustees, Hereford, HR2 9RZ.

407   11.10.11.10

First tune   TU ES PETRUS   *Mode 7: D*

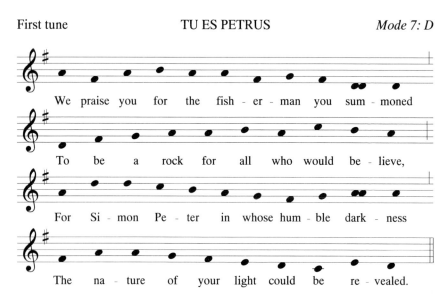

1   We praise you for the fisherman you summoned
     To be a rock for all who would believe,
     For Simon Peter in whose humble darkness
     The nature of your light could be revealed.

2   We pray for healing for the broken Body,
     And unity for all who are baptised.
     We pray for greater love among all Christians:
     Let no one in Christ's Body be despised.

3   O Father, hear the prayer of that one shepherd,
     Who is your Son, our brother and our Lord;
     United in your Spirit may we honour
     The one who brought your peace into the world.

SAINT PETER'S CHAIR

407

Second tune   INTERCESSOR

Text: Ralph Wright OSB, abbreviated. First tune: Alan Rees OSB, based on the antiphon *Tu es Petrus*.
Second tune: C. Hubert H. Parry (1848-1918).

Text: © 1989, GIA Publications Inc., 7404 South Mason Avenue, Chicago, Illinois 60638. All rights reserved. First tune: © 1995, Belmont Abbey Trustees, Hereford, HR2 9RZ.

408   11.11.11.5

First tune   WANTAGE   *Mode 1: D*

Lord, hear the prai - ses of your faith - ful peo - ple

Ga - thered to ho - nour, on this ho - ly feast day,

Jo - seph your ser - vant, guard-ian of the Christ - child,

Hus - band of Ma - ry.

1   Lord, hear the praises of your faithful people
     Gathered to honour, on this holy feast day,
     Joseph your servant, guardian of the Christ-child,
     Husband of Mary.

2   Second in honour to the Virgin Mother,
     Gladly he yielded to his high vocation,
     When in a vision he was told the story
     Of her conceiving.

3   And when the saviour, whom prophetic voices
     Long had predicted, lay within the manger,
     Mother and infant, by his strong protection,
     Rested securely.

4   May his example give to us your servants
     Love of Christ Jesus, bringer of salvation,
     That with Saint Joseph we at length may praise you
     In life eternal.

5   Almighty Father, unto you be glory,
     With Christ our saviour and the Holy Spirit,
     From all your people, here and in your heaven,
     Now and for ever.

SAINT JOSEPH

Second tune   CHRISTE SANCTORUM

Text: *The New English Hymnal*, altered. First tune: Community of Saint Mary the Virgin, Wantage.
Second tune: melody, Paris Antiphoner, 1681; harmony, Ralph Vaughan Williams (1872-1958), from
The English Hymnal.

Text: © 1986, The Canterbury Press, Norwich NR3 3BH. First tune: Community of Saint Mary the
Virgin, Wantage, Oxfordshire. Second tune (harmony): © Oxford University Press.

409   7.5.7.5

First tune   PENHALONGA   *Mode 1: D*

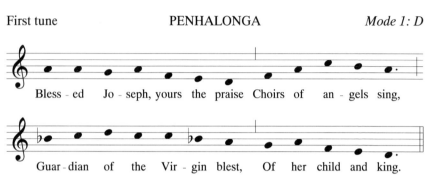

Bless - ed Jo - seph, yours the praise Choirs of   an - gels sing,

Guar - dian   of   the   Vir - gin blest,   Of   her child and king.

Second tune   SAINT AIDAN

SAINT JOSEPH

1   Blessed Joseph, yours the praise
Choirs of angels sing,
Guardian of the Virgin blest,
Of her child and king.

2   Prophets told of Christ to come:
God as man on earth;
Yours the glory there to be
At the saviour's birth.

3   To the Father's only Son
You were father here;
He was subject to your will
Whom the heavens revere.

4   Once you sought and found again
Christ, the Lord of light;
May we walk with him, like you,
Humble in his sight.

5   Father, Son and Spirit blest,
God of truth and grace,
By the prayer of Joseph, grant
We may see your face.

Text: Stanbrook Abbey. First tune: Charles Watson OSB and Peter Allan CR. Second tune: Herbert Popple (1891-1965).

Text: © 1974 and 1995, Stanbrook Abbey, Callow End, Worcester WR2 4TD. First tune: © 1995, Panel of Monastic Musicians, Mount Saint Bernard Abbey, Coalville, Leicester LE67 5UL. Second tune: © Oxford University Press.

410

CM

First tune　　　　　　　　ANGLICANUS　　　　　*Mode 8: G*

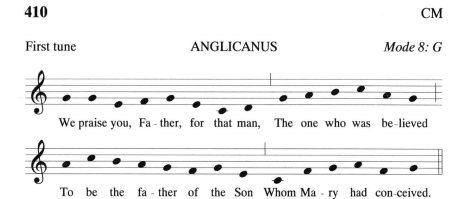

We praise you, Fa - ther, for that man, The one who was be - lieved

To be the fa - ther of the Son Whom Ma - ry had con-ceived.

Second tune　　　MORNING SONG (CONSOLATION)

Alternative: SAINT BOTOLPH, 209

SAINT JOSEPH

1   We praise you, Father, for that man,
    The one who was believed
    To be the father of the Son
    Whom Mary had conceived.

2   He welcomed Mary to his home,
    He helped her bear your child;
    He fled with her from Bethlehem
    Escaping Herod's guile.

3   He cared for Jesus as he grew,
    He led him in your ways;
    And, as a father, taught your Son
    To work with wood and blade.

4   You called him to that narrow road
    That leads beyond the light,
    To trust, compassion, gentleness,
    And patience through the night.

5   O Father, hear the patient prayers
    Of Joseph, through your Son,
    That in your Spirit we may work
    To see your kingdom come.

Text: Ralph Wright OSB, abbreviated. First tune: *The Anglican Office Book*. Second tune: melody, Kentucky Harmony, 1816; harmony, John Harper.

Text: © 1989, GIA Publications Inc., 7404 South Mason Avenue, Chicago, Illinois 60638. All rights reserved. First tune: © 1981, Communities Consultative Council (Anglican Religious Communities), PO Box 17, Eccleshall, Stafford ST21 6LB. Second tune (harmony): © 1995, Panel of Monastic Musicians, Mount Saint Bernard Abbey, Coalville, Leicester LE67 5UL.

411   11.10.11.10

First tune   NAZARETH   *Mode 5: D*

An - gels and se - ra - phim, thrones _ and do - mi - nions

Clus - ter in si - lence on Na - za - reth hill,

All of cre - a - tion stands breath - less with won - der,

Wait - ing the Word that will bring ___ its re - lease.

1   Angels and seraphim, thrones and dominions
     Cluster in silence on Nazareth hill,
     All of creation stands breathless with wonder,
     Waiting the Word that will bring its release.

2   Word of a Virgin who, knowing her weakness,
     Gives herself wholly to God her betrothed;
     Word of the Father, eternal almighty,
     Needing a home in that Virgin's pure womb.

3   Chosen by God at the dawn of creation,
     She stands alone in the silence of faith;
     Maiden of Israel now, but hereafter
     Mother of Christ and his Church through her love.

4   Jesus our Lord, in the whole of your being
     You are the perfect expression of love,
     Word of the Father, who breathes out upon us
     Spirit of tenderness, mercy and truth.

Text: Mount Saint Bernard Abbey, altered. First tune: Alan Rees OSB. Second tune: melody adapted
from *Himmels-Lust*, Jena 1679; harmony adapted from J. S. Bach (1685-1750).

Evening Prayer

411

Second tune   LIEBSTER IMMANUEL

412 7.7.7.7

First tune NUN KOMM' DER HEIDEN HEILAND *Mode 2: E*

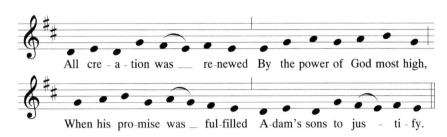

All cre - a - tion was __ re-newed By the power of God most high,

When his pro-mise was __ ful-filled A-dam's sons to jus - ti - fy.

1 All creation was renewed
By the power of God most high,
When his promise was fulfilled
Adam's race to justify.

2 By the Holy Spirit's love
God pronounced his saving Word,
Then with free consent and trust
Mary bore creation's Lord.

3 Moment of unequalled faith,
Here in any time or place:
Thus did God put on our flesh
In his Virgin full of grace.

4 Christ, the holy one of God,
Son of David, light from light,
Dwells on earth, his glory dimmed
Till he comes again with might.

5 Father, Son and Spirit praise
For this marvel they have done;
In this act of perfect love,
Undivided, always One.

When the second tune is used, omit 'Alleluia' in Lent.

Morning Prayer **412**

Second tune ORIENTIS PARTIBUS 7.7.7.7.4

Al - le - lu - ia.

Text: Stanbrook Abbey. First tune: *Erfurt Enchiridion*, 1524. Second tune: melody, *Office de la Circoncision*, Sens, 13th century; harmony, Ralph Vaughan Williams (1872-1958), from *The English Hymnal*, altered.

Text: © 1974 and 1995, Stanbrook Abbey, Callow End, Worcester WR2 4TD. Second tune (harmony): © Oxford University Press. Altered by permission.

413   8.7.8.7.8.7

First tune   CYMER   *Mode 2: G*

Let God's peo-ple join in wor-ship On the glo-rious Mo-ther's feast,

And en-treat the gra-cious fa-vour Of the child she car-ried then,

Whom E - li - za-beth, dis-cern-ing, Wel-comed as the com-ing- Christ.

Alternative: GALLI CANTU, 339

1 Let God's people join in worship
  On the glorious Mother's feast,
  And entreat the gracious favour
  Of the child she carried then,
  Whom Elizabeth, discerning,
  Welcomed as the coming Christ.

2 As the infant leapt with gladness
  At the presence of the Word,
  So Elizabeth, believing,
  Knew the mother of the Lord,
  And in awe proclaimed her blessed
  In the wonder of her child.

3 'How should God's unworthy servant
  Now be given so rich a grace:
  Salutation from the mother
  Of the king of all the world?
  For the prophet child within me
  Leapt in sign of holy joy.'

4 Then the Virgin, God acknowledged,
  Pouring forth her praise in song,
  Glorified with adoration
  Him who saved her by his grace,
  That in every generation
  All his Church should call her blest.

5 Holy Father, Son and Spirit,
  Reigning in eternal power,
  At the prayer of blessed Mary
  Keep us safe for evermore,
  And our earthly course completed,
  Bring us to eternal life.

THE VISITATION OF THE BLESSED VIRGIN MARY

413

Second tune   MANNHEIM

Alternatives: TANTUM ERGO, 149; FORTUNATUS NEW, 304

Text: The Community of the Holy Name, Malvern, altered. First tune: Mount Saint Bernard Abbey.
Second tune: melody, F. Filitz, *Choralbuch*, 1847; harmony, Lowell Mason (1792-1872).

414   CM

First tune   ANGLICANUS   *Mode 8: G*

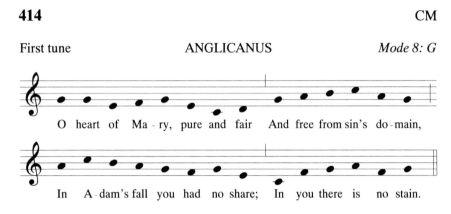

O heart of Ma‑ry, pure and fair And free from sin's do‑main,

In A‑dam's fall you had no share; In you there is no stain.

Alternative: CRANHAM CORNER, 141

Second tune   NUN DANKET ALL

THE IMMACULATE HEART OF THE BLESSED VIRGIN MARY

1   O heart of Mary, pure and fair
And free from sin's domain,
In Adam's fall you had no share;
In you there is no stain.

2   The fairest rose, which grew in thorns,
Your heart so full of grace
With spotless purity adorns
Our sinful fallen race.

3   The heart of Christ, by God's decree,
Was formed beneath your heart,
We long to love him worthily:
In your love give us part.

4   His words you pondered in your heart
With contemplation pure;
O may the grace which they impart,
In our weak hearts endure.

Text: Anonymous, altered. First tune: *The Anglican Office Book*. Second tune: melody, J. Crüger, *Praxis Pietatis Melica*, 1647.

Text (this version): © 1995, Panel of Monastic Musicians, Mount Saint Bernard Abbey, Coalville, Leicester LE67 5UL. First tune: © 1981, Communities Consultative Council (Anglican Religious Communities), PO Box 17, Eccleshall, Stafford ST21 6LB.

415   11.11.11.5

First tune   UT QUEANT LAXIS   *Mode 2: E*

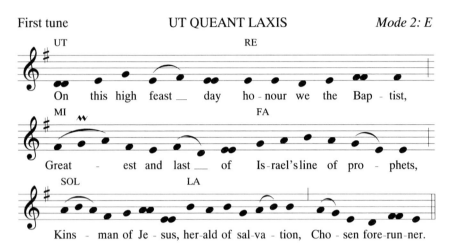

On this high feast __ day ho - nour we the Bap - tist,
Great - est and last __ of Is-rael's line of pro - phets,
Kins - man of Je - sus, her-ald of sal-va - tion, Cho - sen fore-run-ner.

Alternative: O PATER SANCTE, 256

1   On this high feast day honour we the Baptist,
    Greatest and last of Israel's line of prophets,
    Kinsman of Jesus, herald of salvation,
    Chosen forerunner.

2   See, from the heavens Gabriel descending,
    Brings to your father tidings of your coming,
    Telling your name, and all your life's high calling
    Duly announcing.

3   When Zechariah doubted what was told him,
    Dumbness assailed him, sealing firm the promise,
    Till, at your naming, when his voice resounded
    Loud in God's praises.

4   Greater by far than all the sons of Adam,
    Lowly in spirit, faithfully proclaiming
    Israel's Messiah, Jesus our redeemer;
    Now we exalt you.

5   Father eternal, Son, and Holy Spirit,
    God everlasting, hear your people's praises;
    Let saints on earth with all the saints in glory
    Ever adore you.

Second tune   UT QUEANT LAXIS

Alternative: ISTE CONFESSOR, 333

Text: *The New English Hymnal*, altered; from *Ut queant laxis*, Paul the Deacon (c. 720-c. 800). Second tune: melody, Paris Antiphoner, 1681; harmony, John Harper.

416

First tune   IESU, CORONA CELSIOR   *Mode 8: G*

O pro-phet John, O man of_ God, Your love_ was pure as de-sert fire;

Ob-tain for us pure hearts that we ____ May sing_ with voi-ces that in-spire.

Second tune   WINCHESTER NEW

THE BIRTH OF SAINT JOHN THE BAPTIST

1   O prophet John, O man of God,
Your love was pure as desert fire;
Obtain for us pure hearts that we
May sing with voices that inspire.

2   The angel came and brought the word
That soon your mother would conceive;
Your father heard the chosen name
But in his heart could not believe.

3   Through unbelief his tongue was tied,
His voice was silent till that day
When he declared 'His name is John',
And all were filled with deep dismay.

4   While still within your mother's womb
You leapt to greet the hidden Word;
Your mother spoke, alive with joy,
And Mary praised her mighty Lord.

5   To God the Father offer praise,
To Jesus Christ his only Son,
And in their gracious Spirit sing
Of all that God in love has done.

Text: Ralph Wright OSB, altered; from *Ut queant laxis*, Paul the Deacon (c. 720-c. 800). Second tune: adapted from chorale, *Musikalisches Handbuch*, Hamburg 1690.

417

First tune   VENI, REDEMPTOR GENTIUM (ii)   *Mode 2: F*

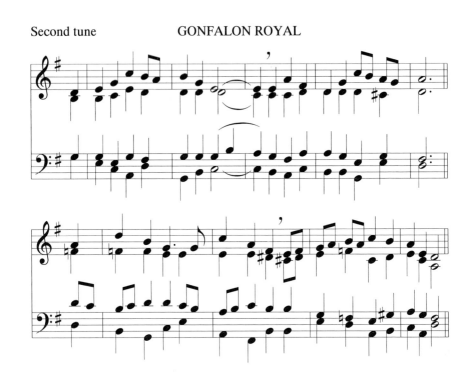

Saint John was like a flam-ing torch, E-van-gel-ist of com-ing light,

Fore-run-ner of the reign of grace, And mes-sen-ger of truth's full right.

Second tune   GONFALON ROYAL

THE BIRTH OF SAINT JOHN THE BAPTIST

1   Saint John was like a flaming torch,
    Evangelist of coming light,
    Forerunner of the reign of grace,
    And messenger of truth's full right.

2   By birth he came before the one
    In whom both God and man combine;
    And in due time he did baptise
    The very source of life divine.

3   As Christ who came to save the world
    Did conquer through a death of shame,
    So too the Baptist shed his blood
    To seal the work for which he came.

4   Most tender Father, grant us grace
    In John's straight way our feet to keep,
    That nurtured in the living Christ
    Eternal joys we too may reap.

Text: Saint Cecilia's Abbey, Ryde, altered; from *Praecessor alme*, Venerable Bede (c. 673-735). Second tune: Percy Buck (1871-1947), harmony adapted.

Text: © 1976, Benedictine nuns of Saint Cecilia's Abbey, Ryde, Isle of Wight PO33 1LH. Second tune: © Oxford University Press; adapted by permission.

418

First tune   ANGLICANUS   *Mode 8: G*

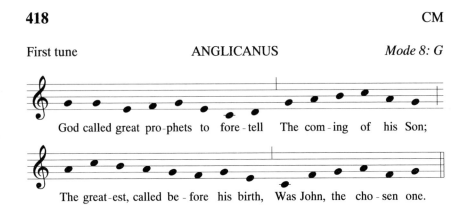

God called great pro-phets to fore-tell   The com-ing of his Son;

The great-est, called be-fore his birth,   Was John, the cho-sen one.

Second tune   MORNING SONG (CONSOLATION)

THE BIRTH OF SAINT JOHN THE BAPTIST

1   God called great prophets to foretell
The coming of his Son;
The greatest, called before his birth,
Was John, the chosen one.

2   John searched in solitude for Christ,
And knew him when he came;
He showed the world the Lamb of God,
And hailed him in our name.

3   That lonely voice cried out the truth,
Derided and denied;
As witness to the law of God
His mighty martyr died.

4   We praise you, Trinity in One,
The light of unknown ways,
The hope of all who search for you,
Whose love fills all our days.

Text: Stanbrook Abbey. First tune: *The Anglican Office Book*. Second tune: melody, *Kentucky Harmony*, 1816; harmony, John Harper.

419

LM

First tune EANSWYTHE *Mode 2: F*

Give thanks for Christ's a - post - les, De - fen - ders of his word,

Who wield through-out the a - ges The Spi-rit's migh - ty sword.

Second tune CHRISTUS, DER IST MEIN LEBEN

SAINT PETER AND SAINT PAUL

1   Give thanks for Christ's apostles,
        Defenders of his word,
        Who wield throughout the ages
        The Spirit's mighty sword.

2   They speak God's word of healing
        Unyielding hearts to move;
        And those by strife divided
        Are reconciled by love.

3   They keep the gates of heaven,
        Have power to loose from sin;
        The bound, set free to meet him,
        With Christ may enter in.

4   To Father, Son and Spirit,
        For these great saints give praise;
        They guide earth's pilgrim-children
        On faith's uncharted ways.

420 LM

First tune O SEMPITERNAE CURIAE *Mode 3: E*

O Pe - ter, ____ you were ____ named by Christ ____

The guar - dian - shep - herd of _____ his ___ flock;

Pro - tect the Church he built on you ____

To ___ stand un - yield - ing, firm _____ on ___ rock.

1 O Peter, you were named by Christ
  The guardian-shepherd of his flock;
  Protect the Church he built on you
  To stand unyielding, firm on rock.

2 Your weakness Christ exchanged for strength;
  You faltered, but he made you true:
  He knew the greatness of your love,
  And gave the keys of heaven to you.

3 Apostle of the gentiles, Paul,
  The greatest witness of them all,
  You turned to Christ, the risen Lord,
  When out of light you heard him call.

4 You journeyed far and wide to tell
  That Christ was risen from the dead;
  That all who put their faith in him
  Would live for ever, as he said.

5 Unseen, eternal Trinity,
  We give you glory, praise your name:
  Your love keeps faith with faithless hearts;
  Through change and stress you are the same.

Second tune   DEO GRACIAS (AGINCOURT)

Alternative first tunes: EXULTET CAELUM LAUDIBUS, 310; FLORES MARTYRUM, 457

Text: Stanbrook Abbey, conflated. Second tune: melody, 15th-century English; harmony, John Harper.

Text: © 1974, Stanbrook Abbey, Callow End, Worcester WR2 4TD. Second tune (harmony): © 1995, Panel of Monastic Musicians, Mount Saint Bernard Abbey, Coalville, Leicester LE67 5UL.

421

First tune · FRATRES, ALACRI · *Mode 1: E*

Our bless - ed fa - ther, ___ Be - ne - dict,

Sure guide _ in dark _ and trou - bled days,

Has shown his count - less chil - dren here ___

The paths of peace, the ___ Lord's own ___ ways.

Second tune · SOLEMNIS HAEC FESTIVITAS

SAINT BENEDICT

1   Our blessed father, Benedict,
Sure guide in dark and troubled days,
Has shown his countless children here
The paths of peace, the Lord's own ways.

2   He dwelt in heaven while on earth,
True man of God and man of prayer;
For him, the love of Christ was all
And God was present everywhere.

3   He left all things that bind the heart,
In poverty to find release;
Unmoved among the things that change,
He sought and found a lasting peace.

4   He died among his many sons
While lifting up his hands to pray.
In glory clothed, he lives again
As we rejoice with him today.

5   Now Benedict, with monks and nuns
Around him, like a crown of gold,
Gives praise to you, blest Trinity,
In splendid light and time untold.

Text: Stanbrook Abbey. Second tune: melody, Paris Gradual, 1685; harmony, John Harper.

Text: ©1974 and 1995, Stanbrook Abbey, Callow End, Worcester WR2 4TD. Second tune (harmony): ©1995, Panel of Monastic Musicians, Mount Saint Bernard Abbey, Coalville, Leicester LE67 5UL.

422   8.7.8.7

First tune   **BATTYEFORD**   *Mode 1: D*

Now is the hour of re - joic - ing: De - sert and waste-land, be glad,

Blos-som with flowers as a gar-den, Wil-der-ness, sing in your joy.

Second tune   **SPRIDDLESTONE**

OUR LADY OF MOUNT CARMEL

1   Now is the hour of rejoicing:
Desert and wasteland, be glad,
Blossom with flowers as a garden,
Wilderness, sing in your joy.

2   Lebanon, Sharon and Carmel
Lend you their beauty and grace;
Bathed in the glory around you,
Gaze on the splendour of God.

3   Eyes that are blind shall be opened,
Ears that are deaf be unsealed,
Feet of the lame shall be dancing,
Lips that are dumb shall sing praise.

4   Rivers shall run in the desert,
Streams in the dry land shall flow,
Lakes shall appear in the wastelands,
Springs in the waterless sand.

5   Now is prepared a king's highway:
Holy is he who shall come,
Ready the way for the ransomed,
Road for the exiles' return.

6   Joyful their journey to Sion,
Homecoming blest with delight;
Gladness shall be their companion,
Sorrow and tears are no more.

7   Mother of Carmel, in glory
Sing to the Father of light,
Sing to your Son, the anointed,
Sing to the Gift of their love.

Text: James Quinn SJ; from Isaiah 35 (1-2, 5-10). First tune: Peter Allan CR. Second tune: melody, Charles Watson OSB; harmony, John Harper.

Text: ©1969, James Quinn SJ and Geoffrey Chapman, a Cassell imprint, Wellington House, Strand, London WC2R 0BB. First tune: ©1995, Community of the Resurrection, Mirfield, West Yorkshire WF14 BN. Second tune: melody, ©1995, Charles Watson OSB, Prinknash Abbey, Cranham, Gloucester GL4 EX; harmony, ©1995, Panel of Monastic Musicians, Mount Saint Bernard Abbey, Coalville, Leicester E67 5UL.

423   11.11.11.5

First tune   QUOD CHORUS VATUM   *Mode 8: G*

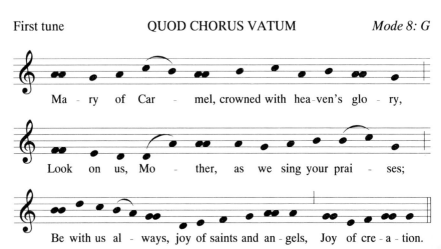

Ma - ry of Car - mel, crowned with hea-ven's glo - ry,

Look on us, Mo - ther, as we sing your prai - ses;

Be with us al - ways, joy of saints and an - gels, Joy of cre - a - tion.

1   Mary of Carmel, crowned with heaven's glory,
        Look on us, Mother, as we sing your praises;
        Be with us always, joy of saints and angels,
        Joy of creation.

2   Here on Mount Carmel peace is all around us:
        Here is the garden where your children gather,
        Praising God's goodness, voices raised in gladness,
        One with our Mother.

3   Come to God's mountain, all who serve our Lady:
        Sing to God's glory, young and old together,
        Full hearts outpouring Mary's song of worship,
        Thanking her Maker.

4   Sing to the Father, who exalts his handmaid,
        Sing to God's Wisdom, Son who chose his mother,
        Sing to their Spirit, Love that overshadowed
        Mary, chaste Virgin.

OUR LADY OF MOUNT CARMEL

Second tune   DIVA SERVATRIX

Text: James Quinn SJ. Second tune: Bayeux Antiphoner, 1739; harmony, Ralph Vaughan Williams (1872-1958), from *The English Hymnal*, altered.

Text: ©1969, James Quinn SJ and Geoffrey Chapman, a Cassell imprint, Wellington House, Strand, London WC2R 0BB. Second tune (harmony): © Oxford University Press. Altered by permission.

424

First tune · AURORA LUCIS RUTILAT (i) · *Mode 8: F*

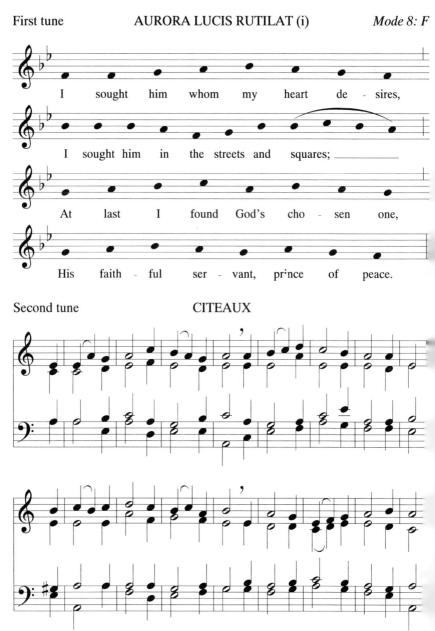

I sought him whom my heart de - sires,

I sought him in the streets and squares;

At last I found God's cho - sen one,

His faith - ful ser - vant, prince of peace.

Second tune · CITEAUX

SAINT MARY MAGDALEN

1   I sought him whom my heart desires,
         I sought him in the streets and squares;
         At last I found God's chosen one,
         His faithful servant, prince of peace.

2   I followed him to Calvary,
         With John I watched beneath his cross;
         His mother too, in silent grief,
         Kept vigil with her dying Son.

3   No comeliness, no beauty there;
         A man despised and put to shame,
         Afflicted for the sins of all,
         And bruised for my iniquities.

4   I lost the sight of him awhile,
         But when the Sabbath day had passed
         I came at dawn in eager haste,
         And saw two angels in the tomb.

5   I wept, distraught, forlorn with grief;
         The gardener spoke - I knew him not;
         But then he called me by my name
         In tones of Christly gentleness.

6   I found him whom my heart desires,
         I kissed his feet in wondering joy.
         How blest are those who see his face
         And live with him eternally.

Text: Mount Saint Bernard Abbey, altered. Second tune: Alan Rees OSB, harmony adapted.

Text: ©1995, Mount Saint Bernard Abbey, Coalville, Leicester LE67 5UL. Second tune: ©1995, Belmont Abbey Trustees, Hereford, HR2 9RZ.

425

10.6.9.6.9.9

WHERWELL

Mode 4: E

Ma - ry, who stayed with your Mo - ther and John,

Shared in your long, last shame;

Saw you in strife with death on the cross,

Call - ing your Fa - ther's name.

Love and truth seemed no more to a - vail,

While __ she watched the dark for - ces pre - vail.

SAINT MARY MAGDALEN

1   Mary, who stayed with your Mother and John,
Shared in your long, last shame;
Saw you in strife with death on the cross,
Calling your Father's name.
Love and truth seemed no more to avail,
While she watched the dark forces prevail.

2   When she came down to your desolate tomb,
Seeking the dead in vain,
Joyful, she heard you, radiant with life,
Speaking her name again.
Then did grieving creation rejoice,
Glad, with her, at the sound of your voice.

3   Father and Son, with the Spirit of both,
God of unending days;
Compassed in glory, Lord over death,
Yours be eternal praise.
Power is yours, who with merciful might
Sin and darkness transform into light.

Text and tune: Stanbrook Abbey.

Text and tune: ©1974, Stanbrook Abbey, Callow End, Worcester WR2 4TD.

426 8.7.8.7.8.7

First tune TIBI, CHRISTE *Mode 2: F♯*

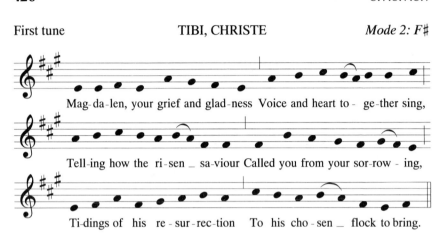

Mag-da-len, your grief and glad-ness Voice and heart to-ge-ther sing,

Tell-ing how the ri-sen _ sa-viour Called you from your sor-row-ing,

Ti-dings of his re-sur-rec-tion To his cho-sen _ flock to bring.

1. Magdalen, your grief and gladness
   Voice and heart together sing,
   Telling how the risen saviour
   Called you from your sorrowing,
   Tidings of his resurrection
   To his chosen flock to bring.

2. She beheld him, yet she knew not
   In the gardener's seeming guise
   Christ, who in her heart was sowing
   Seed of heavenly mysteries,
   Till his voice, her name pronouncing,
   Bade her see and recognize.

3. Weep not, Mary, weep no longer:
   Now your seeking heart may rest;
   Christ, the heavenly gardener sowing
   Living truth within your breast;
   In the joyous cry, 'Rabboni!'
   Be your gratitude confessed.

4. To the Trinity be glory,
   To the Father and the Son,
   With the co-eternal Spirit,
   Ever Three and ever One,
   One in love and one in splendour,
   While unending ages run.

SAINT MARY MAGDALEN

Second tune MANNHEIM

Alternative first tune: GALLI CANTU, 432

Text: C. S. Phillips (1883-1949), altered; from *Collaudemus Magdalenae*, Philip de Greve (d. 1236).
Second tune: melody, F. Filitz, *Choralbuch*, 1847; harmony, Lowell Mason (1792-1872).

Text: © Proprietors of *Hymns Ancient and Modern*, Norwich NR3 3BH.

427   LM

First tune   QUEM TERRA, PONTUS   *Mode 8: G*

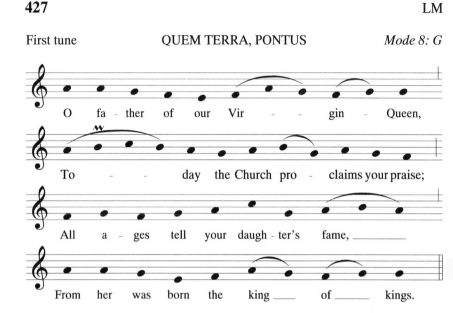

O father of our Virgin Queen,
Today the Church proclaims your praise;
All ages tell your daughter's fame,
From her was born the king of kings.

Alternative: CHRISTE, QUI SPLENDOR ET DIES (1), 113

1   O father of our Virgin-Queen,
     Today the Church proclaims your praise;
     All ages tell your daughter's fame,
     From her was born the king of kings.

2   O blessed Anne, your humble prayer
     Won favour for our sinful race;
     Your grandson, born of David's line,
     Is Jesus Christ, our Lord and God.

3   Eternal Father, God of peace,
     May you be blest in all your saints,
     With Jesus your beloved Son,
     And with the Spirit, Paraclete.

Second tune   **SAINT AMBROSE**

Text: Mount Saint Bernard Abbey. Second tune: La Feillée, *Méthode du Plain-chant*, 1782.

Text: ©1995, Mount Saint Bernard Abbey, Coalville, Leicester LE67 5UL.

428

6.6.6.6

First tune

BETHANIA

Mode 8: E

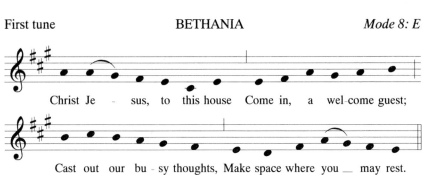

Christ Je - sus, to this house Come in, a wel-come guest;

Cast out our bu - sy thoughts, Make space where you — may rest.

Second tune

AMEN COURT

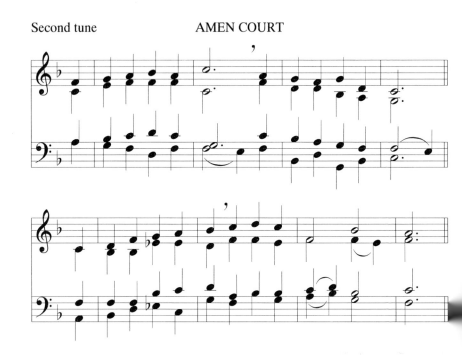

SAINTS MARTHA, MARY, AND LAZARUS

1   Christ Jesus, to this house
Come in, a welcome guest;
Cast out our busy thoughts,
Make space where you may rest.

2   Grant us the peace that brings
Attentive stillness, Lord;
With quiet mind and heart
May we receive your word.

3   You summoned into light
Your friend within his grave,
Restored what all must lose:
The breath of life you gave.

4   O hidden God, whose love
Enfolds and shapes our days,
You are our heart's desire,
Our joy, our song, our praise.

Text: Stanbrook Abbey. First tune: Alan Rees OSB. Second tune: John Dykes Bower (1905-81).

Text: ©1974 and 1995, Stanbrook Abbey, Callow End, Worcester WR2 4TD. First tune: ©1995, Belmont Abbey Trustees, Hereford, HR2 9RZ. Second tune: © The Proprietors of *Hymns Ancient and Modern*, Norwich NR3 3BH.

429   10.7.10.7

First tune   **VALLE CRUCIS**   *Mode 3: E*

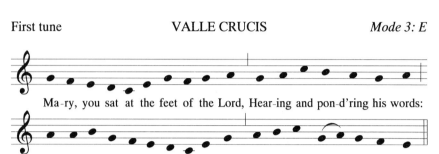

Ma-ry, you sat at the feet of the Lord, Hear-ing and pon-d'ring his words:

Ask him to send us the Spi-rit of truth, Fill-ing our hearts with his peace.

Second tune   **JUCUNDA MINOR**

SAINTS MARTHA, MARY, AND LAZARUS

1   Mary, you sat at the feet of the Lord,
      Hearing and pondering his words:
      Ask him to send us the Spirit of truth,
      Filling our hearts with his peace.

2   Martha, you turned to the Lord in your need,
      Sharing with him your distress:
      Pray that we too may be steadfast in faith,
      Trusting his mercy and love.

3   Lazarus, friend and disciple of Christ,
      Rescued from death by his power,
      Finding new life at the sound of his voice:
      Come to our aid with your prayer.

4   Father almighty, we sing to your name,
      Offering our prayer through your Son,
      Praising your Spirit, the fountain of life,
      Boundless reward of the just.

Text: Mount Saint Bernard Abbey, altered. First tune: Mount Saint Bernard Abbey. Second tune: melody adapted from *Jucunda Laudatio*, A. Gregory Murray OSB (1905-92); harmony, John Harper.

Text and first tune: ©1995, Mount Saint Bernard Abbey, Coalville, Leicester LE67 5UL. Second tune: melody, © McCrimmon Publishing Company Ltd, 10-12 High Street, Great Wakering, Southend-on-Sea, Essex; harmony, ©1995, Panel of Monastic Musicians, Mount Saint Bernard Abbey, Coalville, Leicester LE67 5UL.

430   8.7.8.7

First tune   MARKYATE   *Mode d: D*

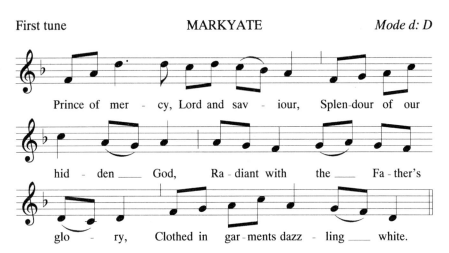

Prince of mer - cy, Lord and sav - iour, Splen-dour of our hid - den ___ God, Ra - diant with the ___ Fa - ther's glo - ry, Clothed in gar - ments dazz - ling ___ white.

Second tune   CROSS OF JESUS

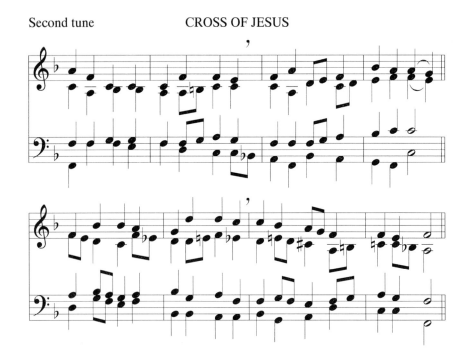

THE TRANSFIGURATION OF CHRIST

1. Prince of mercy, Lord and saviour,
    Splendour of our hidden God,
    Radiant with the Father's glory,
    Clothed in garments dazzling white.

2. Moses and Elijah greet you,
    Speak of mysteries yet to come:
    Cross and heavenly exaltation,
    Mercy to a sinful world.

3. Law and prophets find fulfilment,
    Heights of Tabor shout for joy:
    Peter, James and John in wonder
    Pay their homage to your name.

4. Awesome shadow veils the mountain;
    From the cloud the Father speaks
    Gracious words of revelation:
    'This is my beloved Son.'

5. Prince of mercy, reign for ever:
    Yours be honour, your be praise,
    With the Father and the Spirit,
    Boundless joy of all your saints.

Text: Mount Saint Bernard Abbey, abbreviated and altered. First tune: Stanbrook Abbey. Second tune: John Stainer (1840-1901).

Text: ©1995, Mount Saint Bernard Abbey, Coalville, Leicester LE67 5UL. First tune: ©1974, Stanbrook Abbey, Callow End, Worcester WR2 4TD.

431

LM

First tune   IESU, REX ADMIRABILIS   *Mode d: D*

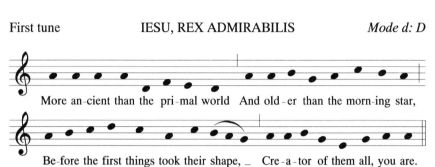

More an-cient than the pri-mal world And old-er than the morn-ing star,

Be-fore the first things took their shape, _ Cre-a-tor of them all, you are.

Second tune   AB ASCENDENTE

THE TRANSFIGURATION OF CHRIST

1 More ancient than the primal world
 And older than the morning star,
 Before the first things took their shape,
 Creator of them all, you are.

2 Your image is the Lord of life,
 Your Son from all eternity;
 All that must perish, he restores,
 In him all reconciled will be.

3 Transfigured Christ, believed and loved,
 In you our only hope has been;
 Grant us, in your unfathomed love,
 Those things no eye has ever seen.

4 O Father, Son and Spirit blest,
 With hearts transfigured by your grace,
 May we your matchless splendour praise,
 And see the glory of your face.

Additional hymn: O raise your eyes on high, 141

Text: Stanbrook Abbey. Second tune: melody, La Feillée, *Méthode du Plain-chant*, 1782; harmony, editors.

Text:©1974, Stanbrook Abbey, Callow End, Worcester WR2 4TD. Second tune (harmony): ©1995, Panel of Monastic Musicians, Mount Saint Bernard Abbey, Coalville, Leicester LE67 5UL.

432   8.7.8.7.8.7

First tune   **GALLI CANTU**   *Mode 2: G*

Do-mi-nic, the Lord's own cham-pion, Charged to spread the Gos-pel flame,

Sent by Christ the word to pub-lish And his myst'-ries to pro - claim;

With the grace of God with-in you, Like a he - ro lord _ you came.

Alternative: TIBI CHRISTE, 426

1   Dominic, the Lord's own champion,
     Charged to spread the Gospel flame,
     Sent by Christ the word to publish
     And his mysteries to proclaim;
     With the grace of God within you,
     Like a hero lord you came.

2   Stainless as a burnished chalice,
     Shining as a fiery brand,
     Dominic, you came to help us,
     And to do your Lord's command,
     With the grace of God within you,
     And the Gospel in your hand.

3   Now again we need your goodness,
     You our father and our guide;
     Keep us from all sin and error,
     From our blindness and our pride;
     With the grace of God within us
     May we stand close by your side.

SAINT DOMINIC

432

Second tune   RESTORATION

Alternative: SAINT THOMAS, 440

Text: M. Owen Lee, altered. Second tune: melody, *The Southern Harmony*, 1835; harmony, John Harper.

Text: ©1957, The Willis Music Company (*New Saint Basil's Hymnal*). Second tune (harmony): ©1995, Panel of Monastic Musicians, Mount Saint Bernard Abbey, Coalville, Leicester LE67 5UL.

433   8.7.8.7

First tune   SIXLAND   *Mode 2: F*

Sing, O Church, our glo-rious mo-ther, Raise your voice in thank-ful love,

For this day a son is gi - ven To the courts of heav'n a-bove.

Second tune   SHIPSTON

SAINT DOMINIC

1   Sing, O Church, our glorious mother,
    Raise your voice in thankful love,
    For this day a son is given
    To the courts of heaven above.

2   Dominic, our guide and leader,
    Father of a white-robed throng,
    Famed on earth for Gospel preaching,
    Goes to swell the angel's song.

3   Loosed from bonds of fleshly prison,
    Now he enters heaven's gate,
    Changing poverty's harsh garments
    For a robe of royal state.

4   Fragrant is his earthly passing,
    And the fame of mighty deeds
    Goes before Christ's faithful servant
    As towards Truth's throne he speeds.

5   Father Dominic, now in glory,
    Plead for those who seek your aid;
    May your prayers for us your children
    Bring us joys that never fade.

6   Praise and honour to the Father,
    Praise and honour to the Son,
    Praise and honour to the Spirit,
    Ever Three and ever One.

Text: Saint Dominic's Convent, Stone, reordered. First tune: John Harper. Second tune: melody, Warwickshire ballad collected by Lucy Broadwood (1858-1929), and arranged by Ralph Vaughan Williams (1872-1958), from *The English Hymnal*.

434

CM

First tune **ANGLICANUS** *Mode 8: G*

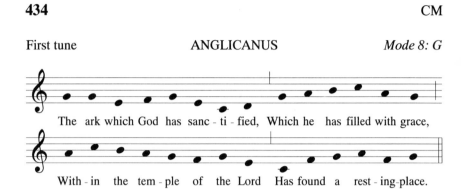

The ark which God has sanc - ti - fied, Which he has filled with grace,

With - in the tem - ple of the Lord Has found a rest - ing-place.

Alternative: CRANHAM CORNER, 141

Second tune **NUN DANKET ALL**

THE ASSUMPTION OF THE BLESSED VIRGIN MARY

1   The ark which God has sanctified,
Which he has filled with grace,
Within the temple of the Lord
Has found a resting-place.

2   More glorious than the seraphim,
This ark of love divine;
Corruption could not blemish her
Whom death could not confine.

3   God-bearing Mother, virgin chaste,
Who shines in heaven's sight,
She wears a royal crown of stars
Who is the door of light.

5   To Father, Son and Spirit blest
May we give endless praise
With Mary, who is queen of heaven,
Through everlasting days.

Text: Stanbrook Abbey. First tune: *The Anglican Office Book*. Second tune: melody: J. Crüger, *Praxis Pietatis Melica*, 1647.

Text: ©1974, Stanbrook Abbey, Callow End, Worcester WR2 4TD. First tune: © 1981, Communities Consultative Council (Anglican Religious Communities), PO Box 17, Eccleshall, Stafford ST21 6LB.

435   11.10.11.10

First tune   POLSLOE   *Mode 7: D*

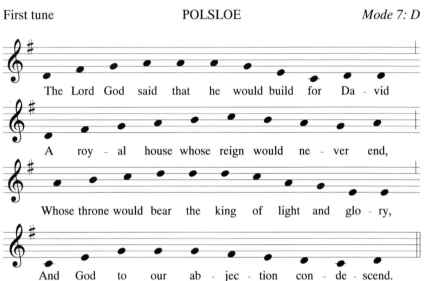

The Lord God said that he would build for Da - vid

A roy - al house whose reign would ne - ver end,

Whose throne would bear the king of light and glo - ry,

And God to our ab - jec - tion con - de - scend.

1   The Lord God said that he would build for David
     A royal house whose reign would never end,
     Whose throne would bear the king of light and glory,
     And God to our abjection condescend.

2   From Jesse's root came forth the Virgin Mary,
     Who bore the world's redeemer, Christ our Lord,
     The Son of God, by his most Holy Spirit:
     His uncreated and eternal Word.

3   Great mystery no thought could ever fathom,
     The saving plan, long fashioned in God's mind,
     When Father, Son and Spirit, undivided,
     Restore immortal life to mortal kind.

THE NATIVITY OF THE BLESSED VIRGIN MARY

Second tune   INTERCESSOR

Text and first tune: Stanbrook Abbey. Second tune: C. Hubert H. Parry (1848-1918).

Text and first tune: ©1974 and 1995, Stanbrook Abbey, Callow End, Worcester WR2 4TD.

436

4.5.4.8

STAINFIELD

Mode 1: D

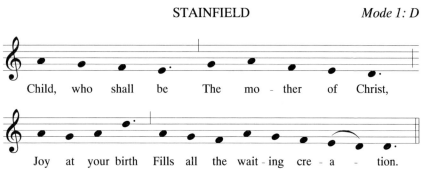

Child, who shall be The mo - ther of Christ,

Joy at your birth Fills all the wait - ing cre - a - tion.

THE NATIVITY OF THE BLESSED VIRGIN MARY

436

1   Child, who shall be
     The mother of Christ,
     Joy at your birth
     Fills all the waiting creation.

2   Like the fair dawn
     That promises day,
     Nearness of Christ
     Shines in the time of your coming.

3   You shall rejoice
     Your spirit exult,
     You shall see God
     Flesh of your pure flesh assuming.

Text and tune: Saint Mary's Abbey, West Malling.

Text and tune: ©1995, Saint Mary's Abbey, West Malling, Kent ME19 6JX.

437   8.8.8.6

First tune   CROXFIELD   *Mode 4: E*

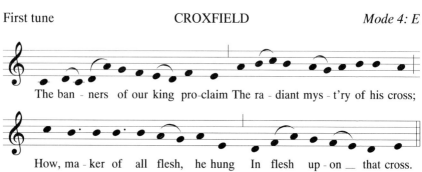

The ban - ners of our king pro-claim The ra - diant mys - t'ry of his cross;

How, ma - ker of all flesh, he hung In flesh up - on __ that cross.

Second tune   TORGAU

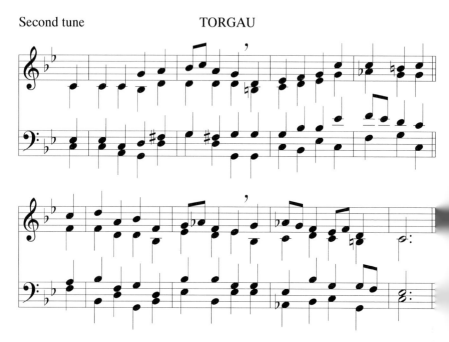

Alternative hymn: The regal, dark, mysterious cross, 146

1   The banners of our king proclaim
     The radiant mystery of his cross;
     How, maker of all flesh, he hung
     In flesh upon that cross.

2   And how his heart was opened wide
     With bitter point of soldier's lance;
     How water flowed with precious blood
     To wash us clean from sin.

3   What David's faithful song foretold
     Was then in very deed fulfilled:
     God reigned, the king of every race,
     His throne the gibbet tree.

4   Most beautiful, most radiant tree,
     With royal purple deeply dyed,
     Whose boughs were fit to bear aloft
     The limbs of Christ our Lord.

5   How blest, because those arms upheld
     The price of ransom for the world;
     As scales they weighed that saving flesh,
     Bought back what hell had seized.

6   We greet you, cross, our only hope,
     Throughout this day's triumphant joy:*
     Give deeper grace to souls in grace,
     New grace to those in sin.

7   Through every age you rule supreme,
     In Godhead one, in persons three;
     And through the mystery of the cross
     Redeem us to your praise.

* *If used in Passiontide*: Throughout this holy passion time.

Text and first tune: Mount Saint Bernard Abbey; from *Vexilla regis prodeunt*, Venantius Fortunatus (c.
30-c. 610). Second tune: adapted from *Ich heb' mein Augen*, Heinrich Schütz (1585-1672), metre
ltered.

Text and first tune: ©1995, Mount Saint Bernard Abbey, Coalville, Leicester LE67 5UL.

438   11.11.11.5

First tune   STROUD GREEN   *Mode 1: D*

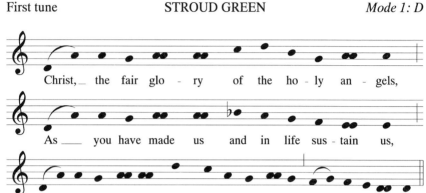

Christ, — the fair glo - ry of the ho - ly an - gels,

As — you have made us and in life sus - tain us,

Grant, of your mer-cy, strength that we may fol-low Your way to hea-ven.

Alternative: O PATER SANCTE, 256

1   Christ, the fair glory of the holy angels,
    As you have made us and in life sustain us,
    Grant, of your mercy, strength that we may follow
    Your way to heaven.

2   Send your archangel Michael to our succour;
    Peacemaker blessed, may he from us banish
    Striving and hatred, so that for the peaceful
    All things may prosper.

3   Send your archangel Gabriel, the mighty;
    May he turn from us all the wiles of Satan;
    Herald of heaven, may he guard the temples
    Where you are worshipped.

4   Send your archangel Raphael to restore us;
    May he anoint us, heal us at your bidding,
    Bringing us strength and comfort on life's journey,
    Guiding us onward.

5   May the blest Mother of our God and saviour,
    May the assembly of the saints in glory,
    May the celestial companies of angels,
    Ever assist us.

SAINT MICHAEL AND ALL ANGELS

Second tune   CHRISTE SANCTORUM

6   Father almighty, Son and Holy Spirit,
       Godhead eternal, grant us our petition;
       Yours be the glory through the whole creation
       Now and for ever.

Text: Athelstan Riley (1858-1945), altered; from *Christe, sanctorum decus angelorum* (9th century).
First tune: Anthony Greening. Second tune: melody, Paris Antiphoner, 1681; harmony, Ralph Vaughan
Williams (1872-1958), from *The English Hymnal*.

Text and second tune (harmony): © Oxford University Press. First tune: ©1995, Elmore Abbey, Church
Lane, Speen, Newbury, Berkshire RG13 1SA; by permission of the abbot and community.

439   10.10.10.10

First tune   TINTERN   *Mode 8: G*

An - gels of God, you see the Fa - ther's face,

Shar - ing his splen - dour, clothed in fire and flame,

Wor - ship - ping him, the ter - ri - ble and great

Sing - ing for - e - ver: ho - ly is his name.

Second tune   BRIXTON TOR

SAINT MICHAEL AND ALL ANGELS

1   Angels of God, you see the Father's face,
Sharing his splendour, clothed in fire and flame,
Worshipping him, the terrible and great,
Singing forever: holy is his name.

Angels, you sang when Christ came down to earth,
Gave him your comfort in the hour of dread,
Solaced his spirit, anguished and alone,
Shouted his triumph, risen from the dead.

3   Angels, archangels, when he comes again,
Compassed in glory, fearful in his might,
Open for him the king's eternal gates:
Then will he lead his faithful into light.

4   When to the Father, Son and Spirit blest,
Angels and mortals glad hosannas ring,
From all creation, from the world unseen,
Up to the Godhead perfect praise will spring.

Text: Stanbrook Abbey. First tune: Mount Saint Bernard Abbey. Second tune: Charles Watson OSB, harmony adapted.

Text: ©1974 and 1995, Stanbrook Abbey, Callow End, Worcester WR2 4TD. First tune: ©1995, Mount Saint Bernard Abbey, Coalville, Leicester LE67 5UL. Second tune: ©1995, Charles Watson OSB, Prinknash Abbey, Cranham, Gloucester GL4 8EX.

440 8.7.8.7.8.7

First tune TIBI, CHRISTE *Mode 2: F♯*

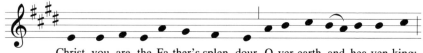

Christ, you are the Fa-ther's splen-dour, O-ver earth and hea-ven king;

In the pre-sence of the— an-gels. Here your right-ful praise we— sing

Du-ly in al-ter-nate chor-us, That our hom-age — we may bring.

1 Christ, you are the Father's splendour,
   Over earth and heaven king;
   In the presence of the angels,
   Here your rightful praise we sing
   Duly in alternate chorus,
   That our homage we may bring.

2 Thus we praise with veneration
   All archangels round your throne;
   Praising first their leader, Michael,
   Heavenly guardian of your own,
   Who in princely virtue banished
   Satan to the realms unknown.

3 By his watchful care repelling
   In the power of your grace,
   Every unseen adversary,
   All things evil, all things base.
   Grant us, Saviour, of your goodness,
   In your paradise a place.

4 Glory be to God and honour
   To the Father and the Son,
   And with them the Holy Spirit,
   Ever Three and ever One,
   Who with joy fills all creation
   While unending ages run.

SAINT MICHAEL AND ALL ANGELS

Second tune   SAINT THOMAS

Alternative first tune: GALLI CANTU, 339

Text: John Mason Neale (1818-66), altered; from *Tibi, Christe splendor Patris* (10th century).
Second tune: Samuel Webbe (c. 1740-1816), *Motetts or Antiphons*, 1792.

441   11.11.11.5

First tune   NOBILEM CHRISTI   *Mode 2: F♯*

Je - sus, our Lord, in - car - nate of a vir - gin,

Made his pure life an of - f'ring to the Fa - ther,

Sin - gle of heart, through dan - ger and temp - ta - tion

Con - stant in pur - pose.

1   Jesus, our Lord, incarnate of a virgin,
       Made his pure life an offering to the Father,
       Single of heart, through danger and temptation
       Constant in purpose.

2   So this true virgin, called to dedication,
       Greeting her saviour's love with love responsive,
       Willingly offered all her heart's allegiance
       Wholly to Jesus.

3   Drawn by the burning visions of his glory,
       Fearing no pain, she gave herself for cleansing,
       That from her weakness he might make a temple
       Fit to receive him.

4   Praise be to God for all her life's example;
       May we his servants, one with her in worship,
       Faithfully follow where our master calls us,
       Filled with his Spirit.

Second tune   DIVA SERVATRIX

Text: *The Anglican Office Book*, altered. Second tune: Bayeux Antiphoner, 1739; harmony, Ralph Vaughan Williams (1872-1958), from *The English Hymnal*, altered.

Text: ©1981, Communities Consultative Council (Anglican Religious Communities), PO Box 17, Eccleshall, Stafford ST21 6LB. Second tune (harmony): © Oxford University Press. Altered by permission.

442   8.7.8.7.8.

First tune   TIBI, CHRISTE   *Mode 2: F*

Je - sus, splen-dour of the Fa-ther, Heart of light, im - mor-tal blaze,

Hear the hum-ble prayers we of-fer Where the an-gels sing your praise;

Hear the soar-ing hymn of glo - ry That in me - lo - dy we raise.

Alternative: GALLI CANTU, 339

1   Jesus, splendour of the Father,
     Heart of light, immortal blaze,
     Hear the humble prayers we offer
     Where the angels sing your praise;
     Hear the soaring hymn of glory
     That in melody we raise.

2   Through these powerful, friendly guardians,
     Christ our king, O drive away
     Every swift deceit of Satan,
     That our frailty might obey;
     Then, with hearts made pure to love you,
     In your kingdom we will stay.

3   Let us praise the mighty Father
     With the Spirit and the Son;
     May our song win hearts to praise them
     Who are Three but also One;
     May the music of our voices
     Share their glory all day long.

GUARDIAN ANGELS

Second tune FORTUNATUS NEW

Alternative: SAINT THOMAS, 440

Text: Ralph Wright OSB, from *Iesu, splendor Patris*. Second tune: melody, Carl F. Schalk; harmony, John Harper.

443   6.6.6.6

First tune   BETHANIA   *Mode 8: E*

With all ___ the poor on earth   For Fran - cis we give praise,

A man who loved true peace,   A flame in fra - gile clay.

Second tune   MARIA JUNG UND ZART

SAINT FRANCIS

1   With all the poor on earth
     For Francis we give praise,
     A man who loved true peace,
     A flame in fragile clay.

2   The more he gave away
     The more God gave again,
     Till, crown of heavenly gifts,
     Christ shared his wounds and pain.

3   Dear father of the poor
     Now make us poor, we plead,
     Until the Spirit's gifts
     Inflame our hearts indeed.

4   All glory, honour, praise
     To Father and to Son:
     Like Francis we too seek
     Unto your throne to come.

Text: Sister Francis Teresa, altered. First tune: Alan Rees OSB. Second tune: *Psalterium Harmonicum*, 1642.

Text ©1992, Convent of Poor Clares, Crossbush, Arundel, West Sussex BN18 9PJ. First tune: ©1995, Belmont Abbey Trustees, Hereford, HR2 9RZ.

444   LM

First tune   IESU, CORONA VIRGINUM   *Mode 8: G*

Most high, om-ni - po-tent, good Lord, To you be cease-less praise out-poured,

From you a-lone all crea - tures came; No one _ is wor - thy you to name.

Second tune   DIE GANZE WELT (HILARITER)

SAINT FRANCIS

1   Most high, omnipotent, good Lord,
          To you be ceaseless praise outpoured,
          From you alone all creatures came;
          No one is worthy you to name.

2   My Lord be praised by Brother Sun
          Who through the skies his course does run:
          With brightness he does fill the day,
          And signifies your boundless sway.

3   By Sister Moon my Lord be praised,
          With all the stars in heaven arrayed.
          Let wind and air, and cloud and calm,
          And weathers all repeat the psalm.

4   By Sister Water, then be blessed:
          Most humble, useful, precious, chaste.
          Be praised by Brother Fire, so bright
          Who lightens, cheerfully, the night.

5   My Lord, be praised by Mother Earth,
          From whom all living things take birth:
          Sustained by you through every hour,
          She brings forth fruit and herb and flower.

6   My Lord be praised by those who prove
          In free forgivingness their love.
          Blest are all those who trials endure
          For you, O Lord: their hope is sure.

7   By Death, our sister, praisèd be:
          From her your people cannot flee.
          Most blest are those who do your will,
          And follow your commandments still.

8   Most high, omnipotent, good Lord,
          To you be ceaseless praise outpoured;
          Let every creature thankful be
          And serve in great humility.

Text: The Community of Saint Clare, Freeland, altered; from *The canticle of the sun*, Saint Francis of Assisi (1182-1226). Second tune: melody, *Kölner Gesangbuch*, 1623; harmony, Redmund Shaw, altered.

Text: ©1995, The Community of Saint Clare, Freeland, Oxford OX8 8AJ. Second tune (harmony): ©1971, Redmund Shaw; by permission of Paul Inwood.

445 7.7.7.7

First tune **MISERICORDIA** *Mode 1: D*

God Al-might-y, mer - ci - ful, To us sin - ners pi - ti - ful,

Of your grace per - pe - tu - al Give the heart to do __ your will.

Second tune **VIENNA**

SAINT FRANCIS

1   God Almighty, merciful,
To us sinners pitiful,
Of your grace perpetual
Give the heart to do your will.

2   Be your will our will's delight;
Cleanse our spirit in your sight,
Warmed and kindled by the light
Of the fiery Paraclete.

3   In the footsteps following
Of Lord Jesus Christ our king,
By your grace alone us bring
To possess you, worshipping.

4   O most high Divinity,
All-enfolding Unity,
Undivided Trinity,
God for all eternity.

Text: The Community of Saint Clare, Freeland. First tune: Alan Rees OSB. Second tune: melody and bass, J. H. Knecht (1752-1817).

Text: ©1995, The Community of Saint Clare, Freeland, Oxford OX8 8AJ. First tune: ©1995, Belmont Abbey Trustees, Hereford, HR2 9RZ.

446 7.7.7.7

First tune   CAELESTIS AULAE   *Mode d: C*

Noon-day blaze of vir-tues rare, High-est gifts of grace_ and prayer,

You have lived in deep re-pose, All that faith on us be-stows.

Second tune   GOTT SEI DANK (LUBECK)

1 Noonday blaze of virtues rare,
  Highest gifts of grace and prayer,
  You have lived in deep repose,
  All that faith on us bestows.

2 Wedded to the Father's Word,
  Word of light, in silence heard,
  Leaning on the Saviour's breast,
  Guided by the Spirit blest.

3 Blest the mind refined by fire
  To receive divine desire,
  Wisdom's secrets in your heart,
  Opened by the heavenly dart.

4 Christ drew you to his embrace
  By the fragrance of his grace;
  In your teaching we confide,
  Trusting you, our heaven-sent guide.

5 Truth eternal, One and Three,
  May Teresa constantly
  Lead us through the mountain ways
  To the realms of joy and praise.

Text: a Carmelite nun. Second tune: melody, J. A. Freylinghausen, *Geistreiches Gesangbuch*, Halle 1704; harmony, William Havergal (1793-1870) and William Monk (1823-89).

447

LM

First tune   CHRISTE, REDEMPTOR OMNIUM (ii)   *Mode 8: F*

O _____ sa - viour ___ Je - sus, Lord ___ of ___ all,

Come ___ save us from ___ our sin - ful ___ ways ___

And through ___ your ___ Vir - gin ___ Mo-ther's ___ prayers

May we _____ her child - ren sing ___ your ___ praise.

Second tune   GONFALON ROYAL

ALL SAINTS

1   O Saviour Jesus, Lord of all,
    Come save us from our sinful ways;
    And through your Virgin Mother's prayers
    May we her children sing your praise.

2   We call on you, O sovereign Powers,
    The armies of the Lord of light,
    From present, past and future sin
    Protect us in the wars of night.

3   We beg you, Prophets of our God,
    And you, apostles of the Word;
    O pray that we may hear that voice,
    And in the Spirit be restored.

3   O pray, you Martyrs of the Lord,
    Who through your blood proclaimed God's Son,
    O pray, all you who spread his reign
    And quietly lived to see it come.

4   O men and women, virgins strong,
    Who gave what you could not afford,
    Now help us to surrender all
    To meet our Bridegroom, Christ the Lord.

5   May all the powers of night be crushed,
    That people may at last be free
    To leap with joy and praise their God,
    Whose Son was nailed upon the tree.

6   To God the Father who creates,
    And to his one begotten Son
    May songs of glory now be raised,
    For in the Spirit all are one.

Alternative first tunes: EXSULTET CAELUM LAUDIBUS, 310: IESU, CORONA VIRGINUM, 326

Text: Ralph Wright OSB; from *Christe, redemptor omnium, conserva,* Helisachar (9th century). Second tune: Percy Buck (1871-1947), harmony adapted.

Text: ©1989, GIA Publications Inc., 7404 South Mason Avenue, Chicago, Illinois 60638. All rights reserved. Second tune: © Oxford University Press; adapted by permission.

448   LM

First tune   STRATA FLORIDA   *Mode 1: D*

The Fa-ther's ho - ly-ones, the blest, Who drank the cha-lice of the Lord,

Have learned that bit-ter-ness is sweet And cou-rage keen-er than the sword.

Alternatives: EXSULTET CAELUM LAUDIBUS, 310; IESU, CORONA VIRGINUM, 326

1   The Father's holy ones, the blest,
     Who drank the chalice of the Lord,
     Have learned that bitterness is sweet
     And courage keener than the sword.

2   In darkness they were unafraid,
     And kept alight their living fire;
     They now keep timeless days of joy,
     Where God gives all their hearts desire.

3   May all that splendid company,
     Whom Christ in glory came to meet,
     Help us on our uneven road
     Made smoother by their passing feet.

4   O Father, Son and Spirit blest,
     May we keep faith till time shall cease;
     Grant us a place among your saints,
     The poor who served the prince of peace.

448

Second tune **REX GLORIOSE MARTYRUM**

Text: Stanbrook Abbey. First tune: Mount Saint Bernard Abbey. Second tune: adapted from *Katholische Geistliche Gesänge*, Andernach 1608; harmony, probably Ralph Vaughan Williams (1872-1958), altered.

Text: ©1974 and 1995, Stanbrook Abbey, Callow End, Worcester WR2 4TD. First tune: ©1995, Mount Saint Bernard Abbey, Coalville, Leicester LE67 5UL.

449

First tune

CHRISTE, REDEMPTOR OMNIUM (ii)

LM

Mode 8: F

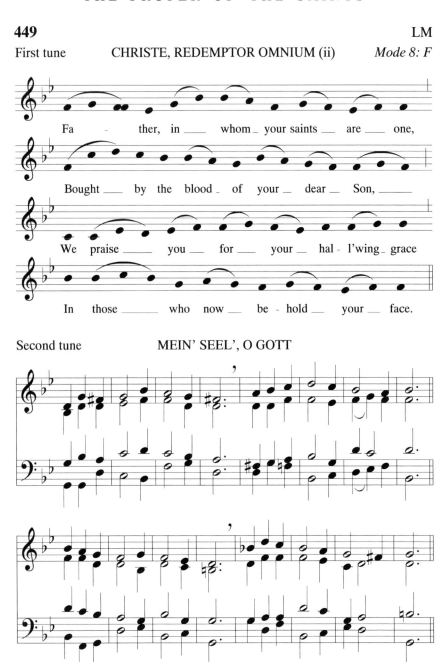

Fa - ther, in __ whom __ your saints __ are __ one,

Bought __ by the blood __ of your __ dear __ Son, __

We praise __ you __ for __ your __ hal - l'wing __ grace

In those __ who now __ be - hold __ your __ face.

Second tune

MEIN' SEEL', O GOTT

ALL SAINTS

1.   Father, in whom your saints are one,
     Bought by the blood of your dear Son,
     We praise you for your hallowing grace
     In those who now behold your face.

2.   For they have gained eternal rest,
     And in the heavenly mansions blest
     They dwell among the angelic throng,
     And hear the one unending song.

3.   The patriarchs and prophets old
     The heavenly splendour now behold;
     The Baptist, herald of your Son,
     Enjoys the fruit of labour done.

4.   But first among the saintly band,
     The Mother, at her Son's right hand,
     Adores the Saviour's endless love,
     In that eternal home above.

5.   The twelve now see the Father's face,
     While all who've run their earthly race
     In one glad company rejoice
     To hear the heavenly bridegroom's voice.

6.   Father of all, to you we pray,
     Keep us forever in the way
     That leads us to the heavenly rest
     Among the glories of the blest.

7.   To God the Father, God the Son,
     And God the Spirit, Three in One,
     All worship, love and honour be,
     Both now and in eternity.

Alternative first tune: IESU, CORONA CELSIOR, 330

Text: G. B. Timms; from *Iesu, salvator saeculi* (10th century). Second tune: Michael Praetorius (1571-1621).

450

10.10.10.10

First tune

RUFFORD

Mode 8: E♭

Let all the earth re-sound with praise this day

For him who took our low-ly hu-man form,

On Cal-va-ry en-dured the shame-ful cross

And broke the bonds of sin for our re-lease.

1   Let all the earth resound with praise this day
     For him who took our lowly human form,
     On Calvary endured the shameful cross
     And broke the bonds of sin for our release.

2   By faith and sacrament espoused to Christ,
     His holy Church acclaims him as her Lord;
     His passion and his cross she makes her own,
     To share at last his triumph over death.

3   Already from her midst a countless host
     Goes forth to meet him, heralding her joy.
     From age to age they come, from every land:
     They are his people, ransomed by his blood.

4   Apostles, martyrs, pastors of the flock,
     Are welcomed home and share their Master's feast;
     While princes, scholars, humble peasant folk,
     Rejoice together in their Father's house.

5   The men who left all things to follow Christ
     Behold him face to face in ardent love;
     And virgins chant their glad Magnificat
     With Mary, maiden queen of all the saints.

ALL SAINTS

Second tune   FARLEY CASTLE

6 Let heaven and earth unite in praise and thanks
   To God our Father, Source of life and grace;
   All glory to our Saviour, Jesus Christ,
   And to the Spirit, bond of peace and love.

Text and first tune: Mount Saint Bernard Abbey. Second tune: Henry Lawes (1596-1662).

451

8.7.8.7

First tune

STONELEIGH

Mode 2: F♯

Ho-ly light on earth's ho-ri - zon, Hope to us the fall-en, bring;

Light a-mid a world of sha-dows, Dawn of God's re-demp-tion, sing.

Second tune

WALTHAM

1   Holy light on earth's horizon,
     Hope to us the fallen, bring;
     Light amid a world of shadows,
     Dawn of God's redemption, sing.

2   Chosen from eternal ages,
     You alone of all our race,
     By your Son's atoning merits
     Were conceived in perfect grace.

3   Mother of the world's redeemer,
     Promised from the dawn of time;
     How could one so highly favoured
     Share the guilt of Adam's crime?

4   Sun and moon and stars adorn you,
     Sinless Eve, triumphant sign;
     You are she who crushed the serpent,
     Mary, pledge of life divine.

5   Earth below and highest heaven
     Praise the splendour of your state:
     You who now are crowned in glory
     Were conceived immaculate.

6   Hail, beloved of the Father,
     Mother of his only Son,
     Mystic bride of Love eternal,
     Hail, most fair and spotless one.

Text: Edward Caswall (1814-78), altered; from *Alma lux* (17th century). First tune: Mount Saint Bernard Abbey. Second tune: melody adapted from Heinrich Albert (1604-51) by Charles Steggall (1826-1905).

Text (this version): ©1995, Panel of Monastic Musicians, Mount Saint Bernard Abbey, Coalville, Leicester LE67 5UL. First tune: ©1995, Mount Saint Bernard Abbey, Coalville, Leicester LE67 5UL.

452   8.7.8.7

First tune   **DUX MARTYRUM**   *Mode 2: F♯*

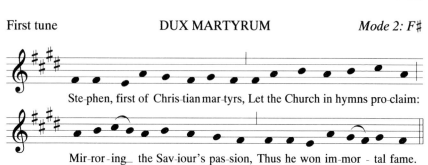

Ste-phen, first of Chris-tian mar-tyrs, Let the Church in hymns pro-claim:

Mir-ror-ing_ the Sav-iour's pas-sion, Thus he won im-mor - tal fame.

Second tune   **WYCHBOLD**

SAINT STEPHEN

1   Stephen, first of Christian martyrs,
     Let the Church in hymns proclaim:
     Mirroring the Saviour's passion,
     Thus he won immortal fame.

2   For his foes he prayed forgiveness
     While they stoned him unto death;
     To the Lord his soul commending
     As he yielded up his breath.

3   Holy Spirit, gift of Jesus,
     Shed thy light upon our eyes,
     That we may behold with Stephen
     That fair realm beyond the skies;

4   Where the Son of Man in glory
     Waits for us at God's right hand,
     King of saints and hope of martyrs,
     Lord of all the pilgrim band.

5   Glory be to God the Father,
     Glory to his only Son,
     Glory to the Holy Spirit,
     Glory, endless Three in One.

Text: *The New English Hymnal*, abbreviated and altered. First tune: editors, adapted from *O qui tuo, dux martyrum*. Second tune: Walter Whinfield (1865-1919).

Text: ©1986, The Canterbury Press, Norwich NR3 3BH. First tune: ©1995, Panel of Monastic Musicians, Mount Saint Bernard Abbey, Coalville, Leicester LE67 5UL.

453   LM

First tune   A SOLIS ORTUS CARDINE   *Mode 3: E*

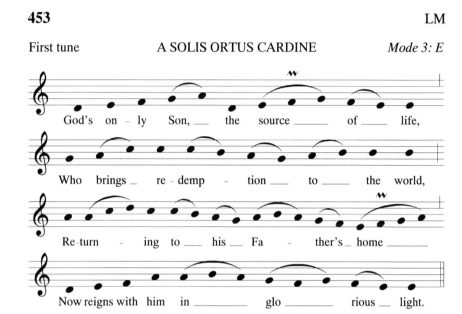

God's on-ly Son, __ the source ____ of __ life,

Who brings __ re-demp - tion __ to ____ the world,

Re-turn - ing to __ his __ Fa - ther's __ home ____

Now reigns with him in _____ glo _____ rious __ light.

Second tune   **SAINT VENANTIUS**

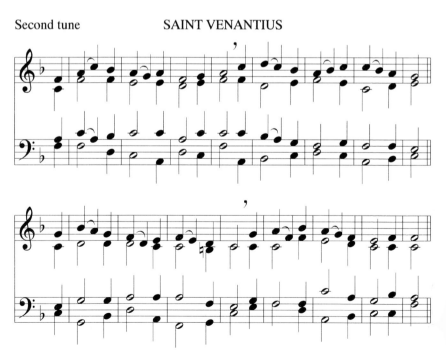

SAINT STEPHEN

1   God's only Son, the source of life,
Who brings redemption to the world,
Returning to his Father's home
Now reigns with him in glorious light.

2   The first to follow in Christ's path
Was Stephen, martyr of the Church.
With faith and hope he faced his death:
God's Spirit filled his heart with strength.

3   Struck down by stones from angry hands,
He met his death without reproach,
Forgiving those who do him wrong:
He shares the triumph of his God.

4   For all who suffer in Christ's name,
Lord, hear us as we pray this day;
Bring justice, peace to all the earth,
And love to every troubled place.

5   Great One in Three, by Spirit made
Incarnate of the Father's will,
With martyr-saints we sing your praise:
Your bond of love has set us free.

Alternative first tune: CHRISTE, QUI SPLENDOR ET DIES (1), 127

Text: John Harper, from *Christus est vita*. Second tune: melody, Rouen Antiphoner, 1728; harmony, Michael Fleming, altered.

Text: © 1995, Panel of Monastic Musicians, Mount Saint Bernard Abbey, Coalville, Leicester LE67 5UL. Second tune (harmony): © 1986, The Canterbury Press, Norwich NR3 3BH.

454 SM

First tune   **SPLENDOR PATRIS**   Mode 8: F

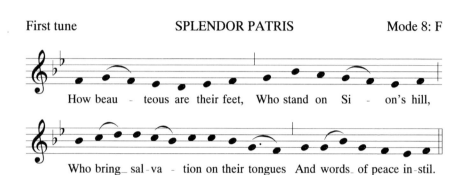

How beau - teous are their feet, Who stand on Si - on's hill,

Who bring sal-va - tion on their tongues And words of peace in-stil.

Alternative: MESSIAH, 102

Second tune   **SAINT EDMUND**

Alternative: FRANCONIA, 102

SAINT JOHN THE EVANGELIST

1 How beauteous are their feet,
Who stand on Sion's hill,
Who bring salvation on their tongues
And words of peace instil.

2 How happy are our ears
That hear this happy sound,
Which kings and prophets waited for,
And sought, but never found.

3 How blessed are our eyes
That see this heavenly light:
Prophets and kings desired it long,
But died without the sight.

4 The Lord makes bare his arm
Through all the earth abroad:
Let every nation now behold
Their saviour and their God.

Text: Isaac Watts (1674-1748). First tune: editors, from *Christe, splendor patris*. Second tune: adapted
from a melody of E. Gilding (d. 1782).

First tune: © 1995, Panel of Monastic Musicians, Mount Saint Bernard Abbey, Coalville, Leicester
LE67 5UL.

455   7.6.7.6.7.6.7.6

First tune   KING'S LYNN   *Mode 1: D*

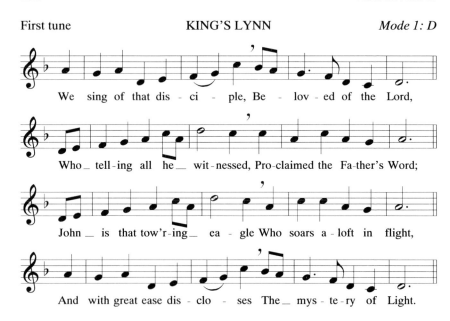

We sing of that dis - ci - ple, Be - lov - ed of the Lord,

Who _ tell - ing all he _ wit - nessed, Pro-claimed the Fa-ther's Word;

John _ is that tow'r - ing _ ea - gle Who soars a - loft in flight,

And with great ease dis - clo - ses The _ mys - te - ry of Light.

Text: Ralph Wright, abbreviated. First tune: English traditional melody.

Text: © 1989, GIA Publications Inc., 7404 South Mason Avenue, Chicago, Illinois 60638.

SAINT JOHN THE EVANGELIST

455

1   We sing of that disciple,
Beloved of the Lord,
Who, telling all he witnessed,
Proclaimed the Father's Word;
John is that towering eagle
Who soars aloft in flight,
And with great ease discloses
The mystery of Light.

2   And when his hour had sounded,
John told how God revealed
The greatness of the Godhead
As Jesus quietly kneeled.
He took their feet and washed them,
As if he were their slave,
And showed the kind of kingdom
That is beyond the grave.

3   Then in the hour of darkness,
When he was stretched alone
Against the Tree in torment
For evil we had done,
He saw the two below him
Who stood there to the end;
And gave each to the other,
His mother and his friend.

4   O sing of that great eagle
The trumpeter of Light,
Who soars beyond the darkness
With mastery of flight.
O sing of that disciple,
Beloved of the Lord,
Whose heart had learned in Jesus
The eloquence of God.

5   We praise you, God our Father,
We praise you, Christ the Lord,
We praise you, Holy Spirit,
Through whom we know the Word;
We pray with that disciple,
The one whom Jesus loved,
That we may share the victory
The victory of Christ's blood.

455   7.6.7.6.7.6.7.6

Second tune   WERDE MUNTER

Text: Ralph Wright, abbreviated. Second tune: from a melody of J. Schop (d. 1644).
Text: © 1989, GIA Publications Inc., 7404 South Mason Avenue, Chicago, Illinois 60638.

SAINT JOHN THE EVANGELIST

1   We sing of that disciple,
    Beloved of the Lord,
    Who, telling all he witnessed,
    Proclaimed the Father's Word;
    John is that towering eagle
    Who soars aloft in flight,
    And with great ease discloses
    The mystery of Light.

2   And when his hour had sounded,
    John told how God revealed
    The greatness of the Godhead
    As Jesus quietly kneeled.
    He took their feet and washed them,
    As if he were their slave,
    And showed the kind of kingdom
    That is beyond the grave.

3   Then in the hour of darkness,
    When he was stretched alone
    Against the Tree in torment
    For evil we had done,
    He saw the two below him
    Who stood there to the end;
    And gave each to the other,
    His mother and his friend.

4   O sing of that great eagle
    The trumpeter of Light,
    Who soars beyond the darkness
    With mastery of flight.
    O sing of that disciple,
    Beloved of the Lord,
    Whose heart had learned in Jesus
    The eloquence of God.

5   We praise you, God our Father,
    We praise you, Christ the Lord,
    We praise you, Holy Spirit,
    Through whom we know the Word;
    We pray with that disciple,
    The one whom Jesus loved,
    That we may share the victory
    The victory of Christ's blood.

456 10.10.10.10

First tune RACHEL *Mode 2: A*

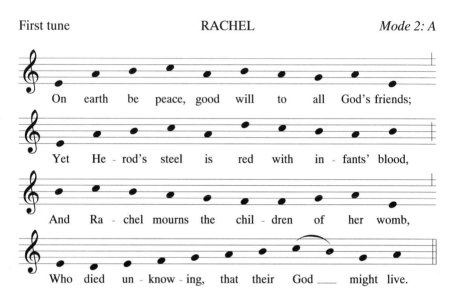

On earth be peace, good will to all God's friends;

Yet He-rod's steel is red with in-fants' blood,

And Ra-chel mourns the chil-dren of her womb,

Who died un-know-ing, that their God _ might live.

1   On earth be peace, good will to all God's friends;
Yet Herod's steel is red with infants' blood,
And Rachel mourns the children of her womb,
Who died unknowing, that their God might live.

2   The first-fruits gathered to the Father's arms,
Their blood has spoken of the new-born king,
Whose peace is not as this world understands,
Whose reign the eyes of faith alone can see.

3   All praise to God whose mercy never ends:
The Father who in love has sent his Son,
That Son who came to free us from our sin,
And sent the Spirit as our guide and friend.

Text: Mount Saint Bernard Abbey, altered. First tune: Alan Rees OSB. Second tune: John Ainslie.

HOLY INNOCENTS

Second tune ELLENBOROUGH

Alternative: FARLEY CASTLE, 450

457

LM

First tune   **FLORES MARTYRUM**   *Mode 8: G*

The mys - t'ry of in-car - nate God   Is sung_ by an-gels in the skies;

Yet He-rod meets him with a sword,_ And Ra-chel for her chil - dren cries.

Second tune   **SAINT VENANTIUS**

HOLY INNOCENTS

1   The mystery of incarnate God
     Is sung by angels in the skies;
     Yet Herod meets him with a sword,
     And Rachel for her children cries.

2   Then stained with sorrow is our joy
     That Christ is born in flesh on earth;
     For shadows of his passion fall
     Across the brightness of his birth.

3   Yet, Jesus, we now give you thanks,
     Because the promise has been given
     That tears shall all be wiped away,
     And love and mercy reign in heaven.

4   And in your new Jerusalem
     Shall hate and love be reconciled;
     And wildest wolf and lion and bear
     Be led transfigured by a child.

5   All praise to you, O virgin-born,
     Made flesh in our humanity,
     To Father and to Paraclete,
     Both now and in eternity.

Text: The Community of the Holy Name, altered. First tune: John Harper, from *Salvete, flores martyrum*. Second tune: melody, Rouen Antiphoner, 1728; harmony, Michael Fleming, altered.

Text: ©1995, The Community of the Holy Name, Morley Road, Oakwood, Derby DE21 4QZ. First tune: ©1995, Panel of Monastic Musicians, Mount Saint Bernard Abbey, Coalville, Leicester LE67 5UL. Second tune (harmony): ©1986, The Canterbury Press, Norwich NR3 3BH.

Ω

LATIN HYMNS

501-515

501

CONDITOR ALME SIDERUM

Mode 4: G

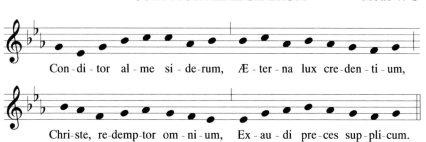

Con - di - tor al - me si - de-rum, Æ - ter - na lux cre-den - ti - um,

Chri-ste, re-demp-tor om - ni - um, Ex - au - di pre-ces sup-pli-cum.

ADVENT

1   Conditor alme siderum,
    Æterna lux credentium,
    Christe, redemptor omnium,
    Exaudi preces supplicum.

2   Qui condolens interitu
    Mortis perire sæculum,
    Salvasti mundum languidum,
    Donans reis remedium,

3   Vergente mundi vespere,
    Uti sponsus de thalamo,
    Egressus honestissima
    Virginis matris clausula.

4   Cuius forti potentiæ
    Genu curvantur omnia;
    Cælestia, terrestria
    Nutu fatentur subdita.

5   Te, Sancte, fide quæsumus,
    Venture iudex sæculi,
    Conserva nos in tempore
    Hostis a telo perfidi.

6   Sit, Christe, rex piissime,
    Tibi Patrique gloria
    Cum Spiritu Paraclito,
    In sempiterna sæcula.

Text: 9th century

502

A SOLUS ORTUS CARDINE

Mode 3: E

A so - lis or - tus car - di - ne

Ad - us - que ter - ræ li - mi - tem

Chri - stum ca - na - mus prin - ci - pem,

Na - tum Ma - ri - a Vir - gi - ne.

CHRISTMAS

1 A solis ortus cardine
   Adusque terræ limitem
   Christum canamus principem,
   Natum Maria Virgine.

2 Beatus auctor sæculi
   Servile corpus induit,
   Ut carne carnem liberans
   Non perderet quod condidit.

3 Clausæ parentis viscera
   Cælestis intrat gratia;
   Venter puellæ baiulat
   Secreta quæ non noverat.

4 Domus pudici pectoris
   Templum repente fit Dei;
   Intacta nesciens virum
   Verbo concepit Filium.

5 Enixa est puerpera
   Quem Gabriel prædixerat,
   Quem matris alvo gestiens
   Clausus Ioannes senserat.

6 Feno iacere pertulit,
   Præsepe non abhorruit,
   Parvoque lacte pastus est
   Per quem nec ales esurit.

7 Gaudet chorus cælestium
   Et angeli canunt Deum,
   Palamque fit pastoribus
   Pastor, creator omnium.

8 Iesu, tibi sit gloria,
   Qui natus es de Virgine,
   Cum Patre et almo Spiritu,
   In sempiterna sæcula.

Text: Cælius Sedulius (5th century).

503

AUDI, BENIGNE CONDITOR

Mode 2: F♯

Au - di, be - ni - gne __ con - di - tor,

Nos - tras __ pre - ces cum fle - ti - bus,

Sa - cra - ta in ab - sti - nen - ti - a

Fu - sas __ quad - ra - ge - na - ri - a.

LENT

1   Audi, benigne conditor,
Nostras preces cum fletibus,
Sacrata in abstinentia
Fusas quadragenaria.

2   Scrutator alme cordium,
Infirma tu scis virium;
Ad te reversis exhibe
Remissionis gratiam.

3   Multum quidem peccavimus,
Sed parce confitentibus,
Tuique laude nominis
Confer medelam languidis.

4   Sic corpus extra conteri
Dona per abstinentiam,
Ieiunet ut mens sobria
A labe prorsus criminum.

5   Præsta, beata Trinitas,
Concede, simplex Unitas,
Ut fructuosa sint tuis
Hæc parcitatis munera.

Text: Saint Gregory? (c.540-604)

504

VEXILLA REGIS PRODEUNT

Mode 1: E

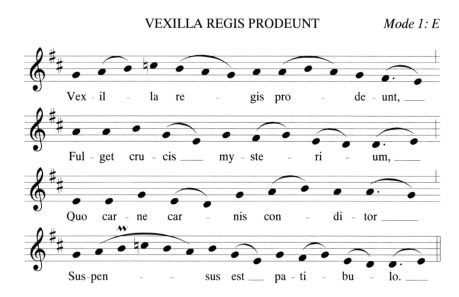

Vex - il - la re - gis pro - de - unt, ____

Ful - get cru - cis ____ my - ste - ri - um, ____

Quo car - ne car - nis con - di - tor ____

Sus-pen - sus est ____ pa - ti - bu - lo. ____

1   Vexilla regis prodeunt,
     Fulget crucis mysterium,
     Quo carne carnis conditor
     Suspensus est patibulo;

2   Quo, vulneratus insuper
     Mucrone diro lanceæ,
     Ut nos lavaret crimine,
     Manavit unda et sanguine.

3   Arbor decora et fulgida,
     Ornata regis purpura,
     Electa digno stipite
     Tam sancta membra tangere.

4   Beata, cuius brachiis
     Sæcli pependit pretium;
     Statera facta est corporis
     Prædam tulitque tartari.

5   Salve, ara, salve, victima,
     De passionis gloria,
     Qua vita mortem pertulit
     Et morte vitam reddidit.

6   O crux, ave, spes unica,
     Hoc passionis tempore*
     Piis adauge gratiam
     Reisque dele crimina.

7   Te, fons salutis, Trinitas,
     Collaudet omnis spiritus;
     Quos per crucis mysterium
     Salvas, fove per sæcula.

Holy Cross: In hac triumphi gloria

Text: Venantius Fortunatus (c. 530-609)

LATIN HYMNS

505A

PANGE LINGUA GLORIOSI (i)   *Mode 3: E*

Alternative   **PANGE LINGUA GLORIOSI (ii)**   *Mode 3: E*

PASSIONTIDE

505A

Part One

1. Pange, lingua, gloriosi
   Proelium certaminis,
   Et super crucis tropæo
   Dic triumphum nobilem,
   Qualiter redemptor orbis
   Immolatus vicerit.

2. De parentis protoplasti
   Fraude factor condolens,
   Quando pomi noxialis
   Morte morsu curruit,
   Ipse lignum tunc notavit,
   Damna lign*i* ut solveret.

3. Hoc opus nostræ salutis
   Ordo depoposcerat,
   Multiformis perditoris
   Art*e* ut atrem falleret,
   Et medelam ferret inde,
   Hostis unde læserat.

4. Quando venit ergo sacri
   Plenitudo temporis,
   Missus est ab arce Patris
   Natus, orbis conditor,
   Atque ventre virginali
   Carne factus prodiit.

5. Lustra sex qui iam peracta
   Tempus implens corporis,
   Se volente, natus ad hoc
   Passioni deditus,
   Agnus in crucis levatur
   Immolandus stipite.

6. Æqua Patri Filioque,
   Inclito Paraclito,
   Sempiterna sit beatæ
   Trinitati gloria,
   Cuius alma nos redemit
   Atque servat gratia.

Text: Venantius Fortunatus (c. 530-609)

505B

PANGE LINGUA GLORIOSI (i) *Mode 3: E*

En a-ce-tum, __ fel, a-run - do, Spu - ta, cla-vi lan-ce-a; _____

Mi - te cor-pus per-for - a - tur, San-guis, un - da pro-flu - it; ____

Ter-ra, pon-tus, as - tra, mun-dus Quo la-van-tur __ flu - mi-ne.

Alternative   ### PANGE LINGUA GLORIOSI (ii) *Mode 3: E*

En a - ce-tum, fel, a-run - do, Spu - ta, cla-vi, lan-ce - a; ____

Mi - te cor-pus per-for - a - tur, San-guis, un - da pro-flu - it; ____

Ter - ra, pon-tus, as - tra, mun-dus Quo la-van-tur _____ flu - mi - ne.

PASSIONTIDE

PART TWO

1. En acetum, fel, arundo,
Sputa, clavi, lancea;
Mite corpus perforatur,
Sanguis, unda profluit;
Terra, pontus, astra, mundus
Quo lavantur flumine.

2. Crux fidelis, inter omnes
Arbor una nobilis,
Nulla talem silva profert
Flore, fronde, germine.
Dulce lignum, dulci clavo
Dulce pondus sustinens.

3. Flecte ramos, arbor alta,
Tensa laxa viscera,
Et rigor lentescat ille
Quem dedit nativitas,
Ut superni membra regis
Miti tendas stipite.

4. Sola digna tu fuisti
Ferre sæcli pretium,
Atque portum præparare
Nauta mundo naufrago,
Quem sacer cruor perunxit
Fusus Agni corpore.

5. Æqua Patri Filioque,
Inclito Paraclito,
Sempiterna sit beatæ
Trinitati gloria,
Cuius alma nos redemit
Atque servat gratia.

Text: Venantius Fortunatus (c. 530-609)

506

AD CENAM AGNI PROVIDI

Mode 8: G

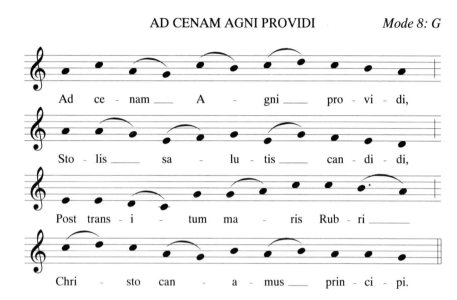

Ad ce - nam___ A - gni___ pro - vi - di,

Sto - lis___ sa - lu - tis___ can - di - di,

Post trans - i - tum ma - ris Rub - ri___

Chri - sto can - a - mus___ prin - ci - pi.

EASTER

1   Ad cenam Agni providi,
     Stolis salutis candidi,
     Post transitum maris Rubri
     Christo canamus principi.

2   Cuius corpus sanctissimum
     In ara crucis torridum,
     Sed et cruorem roseum
     Gustando, Deo vivimus.

3   Protecti paschæ vespero
     A devastante angelo,
     De Pharaonis aspero
     Sumus erepti imperio.

4   Iam pascha nostrum Christus est,
     Agnus occisus innocens;
     Sinceritatis azyma
     Qui carnem suam obtulit.

5   O vera, digna hostia,
     Per quam franguntur tartara,
     Captiva plebs redimitur,
     Redduntur vitæ præmia.

6   Consurgit Christus tumulo,
     Victor redit de barathro,
     Tyrannum trudens vinculo
     Et paradisum reserans.

7   Esto perenne mentibus
     Paschale, Iesu, gaudium
     Et nos renatos gratiæ
     Tuis triumphis aggrega.

8   Iesu, tibi sit gloria,
     Qui morte victa prænites,
     Cum Patre et almo Spiritu,
     In sempiterna sæcula.

Text: Niceta of Remesiana? (5th century).

507

VENI, CREATOR SPIRITUS

Mode 8: F

Ve - ni, cre - a - tor ___ Spi - ri - tus,

Men - tes tu - o - rum ___ vi - si - ta,

Im - ple ___ su - per - na ___ gra - ti - a,

Quæ ___ tu ___ cre - a - - sti, pec - tor - a.

PENTECOST

1   Veni, creator Spiritus,
    Mentes tuorum visita,
    Imple superna gratia,
    Quæ tu creasti, pectora.

2   Qui diceris Paraclitus,
    Donum Dei altissimi,
    Fons vivus, ignis, caritas
    Et spiritalis unctio.

3   Tu septiformis munere,
    Dextræ Dei tu digitus,
    Tu rite promissum Patris
    Sermone ditans guttura.

4   Accende lumen sensibus,
    Infunde amorem cordibus,
    Infirma nostri corporis,
    Virtute firmans perpeti.

5   Hostem repellas longius
    Pacemque dones protinus;
    Ductore sic te prævio
    Vitemus omne noxium.

6   Per te sciamus da Patrem
    Noscamus atque Filium,
    Te utriusque Spiritum
    Credamus omni tempore.

Text: Rabanus Maurus (776-856).

508

PANGE LINGUA GLORIOSI (i) *Mode 3: E*

Pan-ge, lin-gua _ glo-ri - o - si Cor - po-ris my-ste - ri-um, _

San-gui-nis-que pre - ti - o - si, Quem in mun-di pre-ti - um _

Fruc - tus ven-tris gen-er - o - si Rex ef-fu-dit _ gen - ti-um.

Alternative PANGE LINGUA GLORIOSI (ii) *Mode 3: E*

Pan-ge, lin-gua glo -ri - o - si Cor - po-ris my-ste-ri - um, _

San-gui-nis-que pre - ti - o - si, Quem in mun-di pre-ti - um _

Fruc-tus ven-tris gen-er - o - si Rex ef-fu-dit _ gen - ti-um.

THE BODY OF CHRIST

508

1 Pange, lingua, gloriosi
Corporis mysterium,
Sanguinisque pretiosi,
Quem in mundi pretium
Fructus ventris generosi
Rex effudit gentium.

2 Nobis datus, nobis natus
Ex intacta Virgine,
Et in mundo conversatus,
Sparso verbi semine,
Sui moras incolatus
Miro clausit ordine.

3 In supremæ nocte cenæ
Recumbens cum fratribus,
Observata lege plene
Cibis in legalibus,
Cibum turbæ duodenæ
Se dat suis manibus.

4 Verbum caro panem verum
Verbo carnem efficit,
Fitque sanguis Christi merum,
Et, si sensus deficit,
Ad firmandum cor sincerum
Sola fides sufficit.

5 Tantum ergo sacramentum
Veneremur cernui,
Et antiquum documentum
Novo cedat ritui;
Præstet fides supplementum
Sensuum defectui.

Genitori Genitoque
Laus et iubilatio,
Salus, honor, virtus quoque
Sit et benedictio;
Procedenti ab utroque
Compar sit laudatio.

Text: Saint Thomas Aquinas? (1227-74).

509

VERBUM SUPERNUM PRODIENS

Mode 8: G

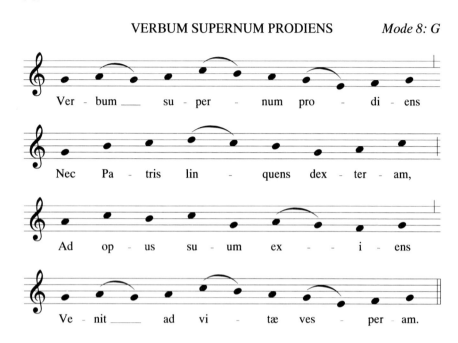

Ver - bum ___ su - per - num pro - di - ens

Nec Pa - tris lin - quens dex - ter - am,

Ad op - us su - um ex - i - ens

Ve - nit ___ ad vi - tæ ves - per - am.

THE BODY OF CHRIST

1   Verbum supernum prodiens
      Nec Patris linquens dexteram,
      Ad opus suum exiens
      Venit ad vitæ vesperam.

2   In mortem a discipulo
      Suis tradendus æmulis,
      Prius in vitæ ferculo
      Se tradidit discipulis.

3   Quibus sub bina specie
      Carnem dedit et sanguinem,
      Ut duplicis substantiæ
      Totum cibaret hominem.

4   Se nascens dedit socium,
      Convescens in edulium,
      Se moriens in pretium,
      Se regnans dat in præmium.

5   O salutaris hostia,
      Quæ cæli pandis ostium,
      Bella premunt hostilia:
      Da robur, fer auxilium.

6   Uni trinoque Domino
      Sit sempiterna gloria,
      Qui vitam sine termino
      Nobis donet in patria.

Text: Saint Thomas Aquinas (1227-74)

510

ECCE IAM NOCTIS

Mode 4: G

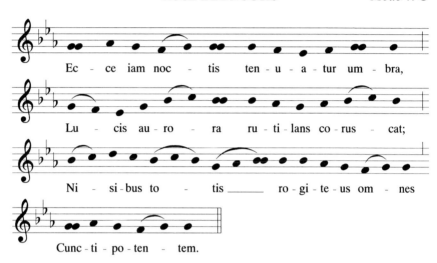

Ec - ce iam noc - tis ten - u - a - tur um - bra,

Lu - cis au - ro - ra ru - ti - lans co - rus - cat;

Ni - si - bus to - tis _____ ro - gi - te - us om - nes

Cunc - ti - po - ten - tem.

1   Ecce iam noctis tenuatur umbra,
Lucis aurora rutilans coruscat;
Nisibus totis rogitemus omnes
Cunctipotentem.

2   Ut Deus, nostri miseratus, omnem
Pellat angorem, tribuat salutem,
Donet et nobis pietate Patris
Regna polorum.

3   Præstet hoc nobis Deitas beata
Patris ac Nati, pariterque Sancti
Spiritus, cuius resonat per omnem
Gloria mundum.

Text: Alcuin? (c. 735-804)

511

LUCIS CREATOR OPTIME

Mode 8: E♭

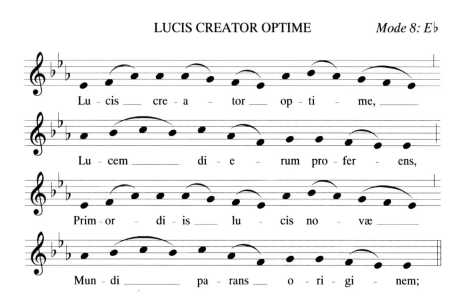

Lu - cis ___ cre - a - tor ___ op - ti - me, ___

Lu - cem ___ di - e - rum pro - fer - ens,

Prim - or - di - is ___ lu - cis no - væ ___

Mun - di ___ pa - rans ___ o - ri - gi - nem;

1 Lucis creator optime,
  Lucem dierum proferens,
  Primordiis lucis novæ
  Mundi parans originem;

2 Qui mane iunctum vesperi
  Diem vocari præcipis:
  Tætrum chaos illabitur;
  Audi preces cum fletibus.

3 Ne mens gravata crimine
  Vitæ sit exsul munere,
  Dum nil perenne cogitat
  Seseque culpis illigat.

4 Cælorum pulset intimum,
  Vitale tollat præmium;
  Vitemus omne noxium,
  Purgemus omne pessimum.

5 Præsta, Pater piissime,
  Patrique compar Unice,
  Cum Spiritu Paraclito
  Regnans per omne sæculum.

Text: Saint Gregory? (c.540-604)

512

COMPLINE MELODIES (SALISBURY)

A: On Sundays and feastdays   *Mode 8: G*

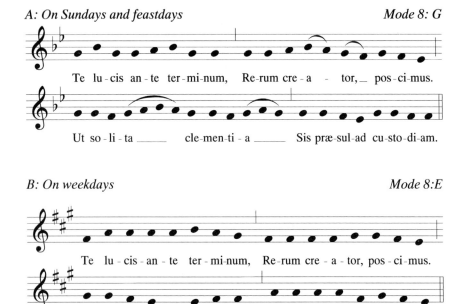

Te lu-cis an-te ter-mi-num, Re-rum cre-a - tor, _ pos-ci-mus.

Ut so-li-ta _____ cle-men-ti - a _____ Sis præ-sul-ad cu-sto-di-am.

B: On weekdays   *Mode 8:E*

Te lu-cis-an-te ter-mi-num, Re-rum cre-a-tor, pos-ci-mus.

Ut so-li-ta cle-men-ti - a Sis præ-sul ad cu-sto-di-am.

Alternatives: COMPLINE MELODIES, 513

COMPLINE

1   Te lucis ante terminum,
Rerum creator, poscimus,
Ut solita clementia
Sis præsul ad custodiam.

2   Te corda nostra somnient,
Te per soporem sentiant,
Tuamque semper gloriam
Vicina luce concinant.

3   Vitam salubrem tribue,
Nostrum calorem refice,
Tætram noctis caliginem
Tua collustret claritas.

4   Præsta, Pater omnipotens,
Per Iesum Christum Dominum
Qui tecum in perpetuum
Regnat cum Sancto Spiritu.

Text: 5th or 6th century, as revised in *Liber Hymnarius.*

513

COMPLINE MELODIES

A: On Sundays   *Mode 8: G*

Chris - te, qui splen-dor et di - es, Noc-tis te - ne-bras — de - te -gis,

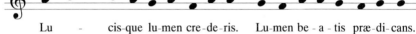

Lu - cis-que lu-men cre-de-ris. Lu-men be - a - tis præ-di-cans.

B: On feastdays   *Mode 2:A*

Chris-te, — qui splen-dor — et di - es, Noc-tis te - ne-bras de - te-gis,

Lu -cis-que lu-men cre-de -ris. Lu-men — be - a - tis — præ-di-cans.

Alternatives: COMPLINE MELODIES (SALISBURY), 512

COMPLINE

1   Christe, qui splendor et dies,
     Noctis tenebras detegis,
     Lucisque lumen crederis,
     Lumen beatis prædicans.

2   Precamur, sancte Domine,
     Hac nocte nos custodias;
     Sit nobis in te requies,
     Quietas horas tribue.

3   Somno si dantur oculi,
     Cor semper ad te vigilet;
     Tuaque dextra protegat
     Fideles, qui te diligunt.

4   Defensor noster, aspice,
     Insidiantes reprime,
     Guberna tuos famulos,
     Quos sanguine mercatus es.

5   Sit, Christe, rex piissime,
     Tibi Patrique gloria,
     Cum Spiritu Paraclito,
     In sempiterna sæcula.

Text: 5th or 6th century

514

URBS IERUSALEM BEATA   *Mode 2: F*

Urbs Ie - ru - sa - lem be - a - ta   Dic - ta pa - cis vi - si - o,

Quæ con-stru - i - tur in cæ - lis   Vi - vis ex la - pi - di-bus,

An - ge - lis-que co-ro-na-ta   Si-cut spon - sa ____ co-mi-te.

DEDICATION OF A CHURCH

1   Urbs Ierusalem beata,
     Dicta pacis visio,
     Quæ construitur in cælis
     Vivis ex lapidibus,
     Angelisque coronata
     Sicut sponsa comite.

2   Nova veniens e cælo,
     Nuptiali thalamo
     Præparata, ut intacta
     Copuletur Domino.
     Plateæ et muri eius
     Ex auro purissimo;

3   Portæ nitent margaritis
     Adytis patentibus,
     Et virtute meritorum
     Illuc introducitur
     Omnis qui ob Christi nomen
     Hic in mundo premitur.

4   Tunsionibus, pressuris
     Expoliti lapides
     Suis coaptantur locis
     Per manum artificis;
     Disponuntur permansuri
     Sacris ædificiis.

5   Gloria et honor Deo
     Usquequaque altissimo,
     Una Patri Filioque
     Atque Sancto Flamini,
     Quibus laudes et potestas
     Per æterna sæcula.

Text: 8th or 9th century

515

AVE MARIS STELLA

Mode 1: D

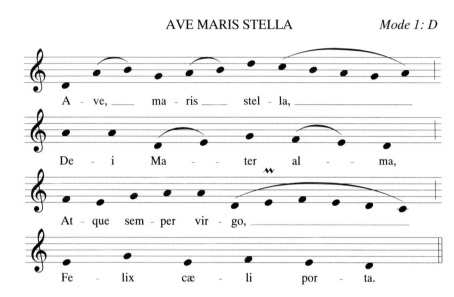

A - ve, ___ ma - ris ___ stel - la, ___

De - i Ma - - ter al - - ma,

At - que sem - per vir - go, ___

Fe - lix cæ - li por - ta.

THE BLESSED VIRGIN MARY

1 Ave, maris stella,
   Dei mater alma,
   Atque semper virgo,
   Felix cæli porta.

2 Sumens illud 'Ave'
   Gabrielis ore,
   Funda nos in pace,
   Mutans Evæ nomen.

3 Solve vincla reis,
   Profer lumen cæcis,
   Mala nostra pelle,
   Bona cuncta posce.

4 Monstra te esse matrem,
   Sumat per te precem
   Qui pro nobis natus
   Tulit esse tuus.

5 Virgo singularis,
   Inter omnes mitis,
   Nos culpis solutos
   Mites fac et castos.

6 Vitam præsta puram,
   Iter para tutum,
   Ut videntes Iesum
   Semper collætemur.

7 Sit laus Deo Patri,
   Summo Christo decus,
   Spiritui Sancto
   Honor, tribus unus.

Text: 8th century

Ω

INDEXES

The Temporal

The Diurnal

The Common

The Proper of the Saints

Latin Hymns

SEASONS, DAYS AND FEASTS

II: AUTHORS AND TRANSLATORS
OF ENGLISH TEXTS

III: COMPOSERS, ARRANGERS AND MUSICAL SOURCES

Numbers in italics indicate harmonization or arrangement

Plainsong melodies are printed in *italic*.
Simplified plainsong melodies are indicated by an asterisk (*).

V. SECOND TUNES
ALPHABETICAL INDEX

SECOND TUNES: ALPHABETICAL INDEX

VI: FIRST TUNES
METRICAL INDEX

Plainsong melodies are printed in *italic*.
Simplified plainsong melodies are indicated by an asterisk (*).

VII: SECOND TUNES
METRICAL INDEX

VIII: FIRST LINES AND TUNES
ALPHABETICAL INDEX

Plainsong melodies are printed in *italic*.
Simplified plainsong melodies are indicated by an asterisk (*).

1